YOU'RE READING THE WRONG WAY

RADIANT reads from right to left, starting in the upper-right corner, meaning that action, sound effects, and word-balloon order are completely reversed from English order.

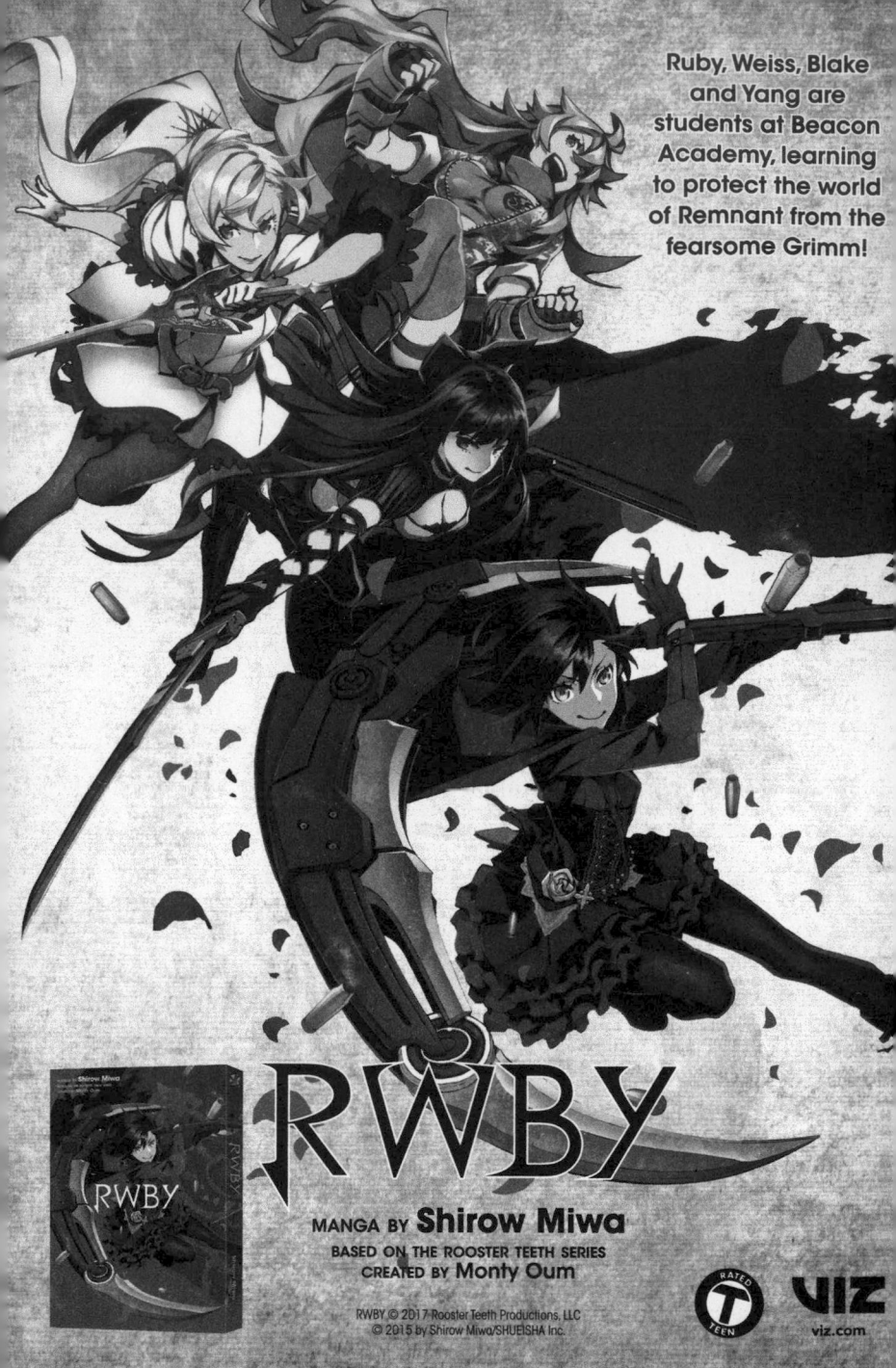

KAGUYA-SAMA
LOVE IS WAR

STORY & ART BY AKA AKASAKA

As leaders of their prestigious academy's student council, Kaguya and Miyuki are the elite of the elite! But it's lonely at the top... Luckily for them, they've fallen in love! There's just one problem—they both have too much pride to admit it. And so begins the daily scheming to get the object of their affection to confess their romantic feelings first...

Love is a war you win by losing.

viz.com

Dr. STONE

STORY BY
RIICHIRO INAGAKI

ART BY
BOICHI

One fateful day, all of humanity turned to stone. Many millennia later, Taiju frees himself from petrification and finds himself surrounded by statues. The situation looks grim—until he runs into his science-loving friend Senku! Together they plan to restart civilization with the power of science!

ASTRA
LOST IN SPACE

CAN EIGHT TEENAGERS FIND THEIR WAY HOME FROM 5,000 LIGHT-YEARS AWAY?

It's the year 2063, and interstellar space travel has become the norm. Eight students from Caird High School and one child set out on a routine planet camp excursion. While there, the students are mysteriously transported 5,000 light-years away to the middle of nowhere! Will they ever make it back home?!

DEMON SLAYER

KIMETSU NO YAIBA

Story and Art by

KOYOHARU GOTOUGE

In Taisho-era Japan, kindhearted Tanjiro Kamado makes a living selling charcoal. But his peaceful life is shattered when a demon slaughters his entire family. His little sister Nezuko is the only survivor, but she has been transformed into a demon herself! Tanjiro sets out on a dangerous journey to find a way to return his sister to normal and destroy the demon who ruined his life.

Black ✽ Clover

STORY & ART BY YŪKI TABATA

Asta is a young boy who dreams of becoming the greatest mage in the kingdom. Only one problem—he can't use any magic! Luckily for Asta, he receives the incredibly rare five-leaf clover grimoire that gives him the power of anti-magic. Can someone who can't use magic really become the Wizard King? One thing's for sure—Asta will never give up!

LVL 1

LVL 1

I love RPGs. What I really love is the exploration! Finding a nice spot, sitting there for a few minutes and looking at it from every possible angle... I basically go full-on tourist. I have a problem with the fights, though. I don't like them so I just avoid them. After a while, I'll know every part of the map! But any and all monsters beat me to a pulp. I love RPGs. I run away a lot in them.

—Tony Valente

Tony Valente began working as a comic artist with the series *The Four Princes of Ganahan*, written by Raphael Drommelschlager. He then launched a new three-volume project, *Hana Attori*, after which he produced *S.P.E.E.D. Angels*, a series written by Didier Tarquin and colored by Pop.

In preparation for *Radiant*, he relocated to Canada. Through confronting caribou and grizzlies, he gained the wherewithal to train in obscure manga techniques. Since then, his eating habits have changed, his lifestyle became completely different and even his singing voice has changed a bit!

RADIANT VOL. 5
VIZ MEDIA Manga Edition

STORY AND ART BY **TONY VALENTE**

Translation/(´・∀・`)サァ?
Touch-Up Art & Lettering/**Erika Terriquez**
Design/**Julian [JR] Robinson**
Editor/**Marlene First**

Published by arrangement with MEDIATOON LICENSING/Ankama.
RADIANT T05
© ANKAMA EDITIONS 2016, by Tony Valente
All rights reserved

Printed in the U.S.A.

Published by VIZ Media, LLC
P.O. Box 77010
San Francisco, CA 94107

10 9 8 7 6 5 4 3 2 1
First printing, May 2019

viz.com

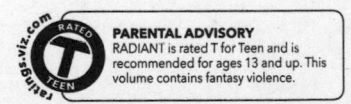

Raxorm Rexkno : Hi, Tony. So here goes: I am seriously a fan of *Radiant* and I'm considering becoming a manga author. Do you have any advice to give me to achieve my dream?

Tony Valente : So there's a gazillion ways of writing storyboards. You can just go by feeling, analyze other manga you like, or even look for techniques that other writers give in classes, workshop, books and so on... But the one thing that creators all have in common is that at one point they all started sharing their work, be it with an editor or selfpublishing. So first, you need to start writing, and then sharing!

And just like any marathon runner who trains to run all 26 miles, you need to start writing before storyboarding your first 50-volume series! Meet your characters, give them solid personalities, love them because you spend so much time with them. Find a story that you think is important and tests your heroes, find something that'll keep your job interesting every step of the way... Be ready to write. Like a lot!

Cassandra. L : Do you think *Radiant* will ever get its own anime?

Tony Valente : Nothing set yet, but I'd love it if it did!

Radiant is now available in two version, one in French and the other in Japanese. (That's so cool!!!) Any other versions planned besides these two?

Regarding foreign editions, right now there's French, Japanese, Spanish and German editions! (This kind of feels like the start of a bad joke...) There's some other countries being discussed too, but nothing's signed just yet, so I'll leave it at that!

Will there ever be any merch from the manga?

There are a few projects going, so fingers crossed!

We can already see that Seth, Mélie, Mister Boobrie, Doc and Grimm are a team. Will Seth's crew be joined by any other allies along the way?

If all goes according to plan, not just one!

Which character do you most identify with?

The character with whom I share the highest amount of mutual character traits is without a doubt Seth. But there's a little bit of me in every one of my characters. And there's a little bit of them inside me as well. Wait, that makes no sense! °_°

Have you ever worn two ties like Doc?

I definitely have. Right now I'm actually wearing eight ties! When I put them back and I start running a bit, they look like a cape! I'm so cool with my eight ties.

Send your questions to: radiant@ankama.com

QUESTIONS...

ANSWERS!!

Raphaël, an "avid reader fan": There's a character in *Radiant* that intrigues me almost just as much as Grimm. I'm talking about Dragunov (that name suits him perfectly btw). I feel like he's a captain who refused the rank of commander and we can see all throughout the chapter that he's got ideas and a way of thinking that's the opposite to his allies. How did he lose his left eye (we can see in a flashback that he used to have both eyes)? Where does his "eagle eyes" come from? I thought he might have an infection, but is that even possible?

Tony Valente : When I first created Dragunov, I immediately thought of a kind of bow and arrow sniper so the great eyesight was par for the course. He's someone who observes things from afar and stays away from all the action, but strikes at the best time. And I extended that character trait to his entire personality. So now we have a man who would rather take on less responsibility to keep his distance from potential problems, but who can also take action when necessary. And I'm glad you mentioned your idea that it might be an Infection, because a lot of people think it is! Some even think that Dragunov is hiding a small iris under his eye patch. But the Inquisition doesn't allow any infected people to join them! One of the attempts at collaboration between infected and the Inquisition was shown in Hameline's past. As for the loss of his eye? I'd love to go into more detail later in the story… As for the secret behind his silky smooth hair? It's an oil from… Oh wait, no, **that's** too top secret.

Justine Laforge : The Inquisition's symbol's been bothering me. Is there any meaning behind it?

Tony Valente : Yes.

I was intrigued by Hameline storing her Nemeses in a piece of parchment. Can the Nemeses see from the inside of the parchment? Can you also store a human?

Good question! Based off of Seth and the others' reaction, you can easily guess that storing Nemeses in a parchment isn't exactly something anyone can do! And storing humans? *Ha haaa*! Who knows!

How old is everyone? Actually, I started wondering about that when I saw Dragunov, whose age I just can't seem to figure out (then again, I've always sucked at guessing people's age!).

Between 17 and 853 years old. Give or take one or two bananas.

Oh crap, my presents! No way they'll let me take those in the plane.

Brought back a ton of souvenirs.

Time to go!

Fruits Fish snacks

Visited some amazing places!

ART BOOKS

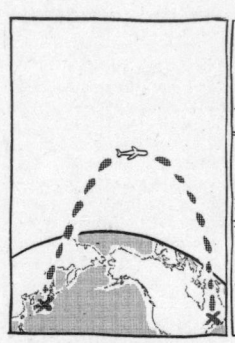

Ate too many souvenirs...

?PORT

Business cards

What's in here?

No, don't...

Look at all the gifts!

It's all for you, sweetie.

?

Next time, I'll be prepared!

?

It was such an amazing experience!

Last November, my editor sent me to Tokyo for the release of the second volume of *Radiant* in Japan.

Met a ton of authors from all around the world.

Got business cards.

Met a ton of bookstore clerks.

Thank you for the attention you give to my manga!

Got business cards.

I signed a ton of books!

Got business cards.

Got a ton of gifts.

Met and talked to a ton of readers!

"At first glance, Radiant looks like a Japanese manga, but its story also includes a slightly more bitter tone that comes from its European roots."
- Hiro Mashima, creator of *Fairy Tail* and *Edens Zero*

TO BE CONTINUED...

I'VE BEEN...!

...POISONED...

IN THE MIDDLE OF THAT FIELD... THAT'S ME?!

WHAT IS THIS?!

THE BARRIER IS SOME KIND OF PROJECTION SPELL?

...I RISK CRUSHING EVERYONE AROUND ME...

IF, I MOVE EVEN JUST ONE BIT...

I JUST NEED TO FIND SOMETHING! AND NOT MOVE!!

ALL RIGHT! SO LONG AS I JUST STAY STILL, EVERYTHING WILL BE FINE!

I CAN FIGURE THIS OUT!

CRAP!

THERE'S A SECOND SPECTRUM

WATCH OUT!!

?!

DAM-MIT!!

HE'S SENSING ME?

A YOUNG MAN, AVERAGE BUILD...

NO ARMS VISIBLE...

A STONE IN HIS LEFT POCKET...

AND... NO!!

WHOA, SLOW DOWN! THIS HAS TO BE A MISTAKE!!

I'M NOT AFTER ANYONE!

I JUST HAPPENED TO FIND THE PASSAGE BY COINCIDENCE!

NO! NOOO!!

HORNS?!

NO, I'M SURE OF IT...

I DON'T KNOW HOW YOU FOUND ME...

...YOUR APPEARANCE IS PROOF ENOUGH!

I'D RATHER DIE THAN—

I ESCAPED FROM HIM! I SHOULD HAVE BEEN SAFE WITHIN THESE WALLS!

ONLY, THIS ONE IS MUCH SMALLER...

THAT, LOOKS EXACTLY, LIKE THE NEMESIS FROM BEFORE!

TIK TIK TIK

?!

WHO'S THERE ?!

CRAP!

VRZZZ VRZZZ VRZZZ

GZZZ

CANFOD— LOCATE!

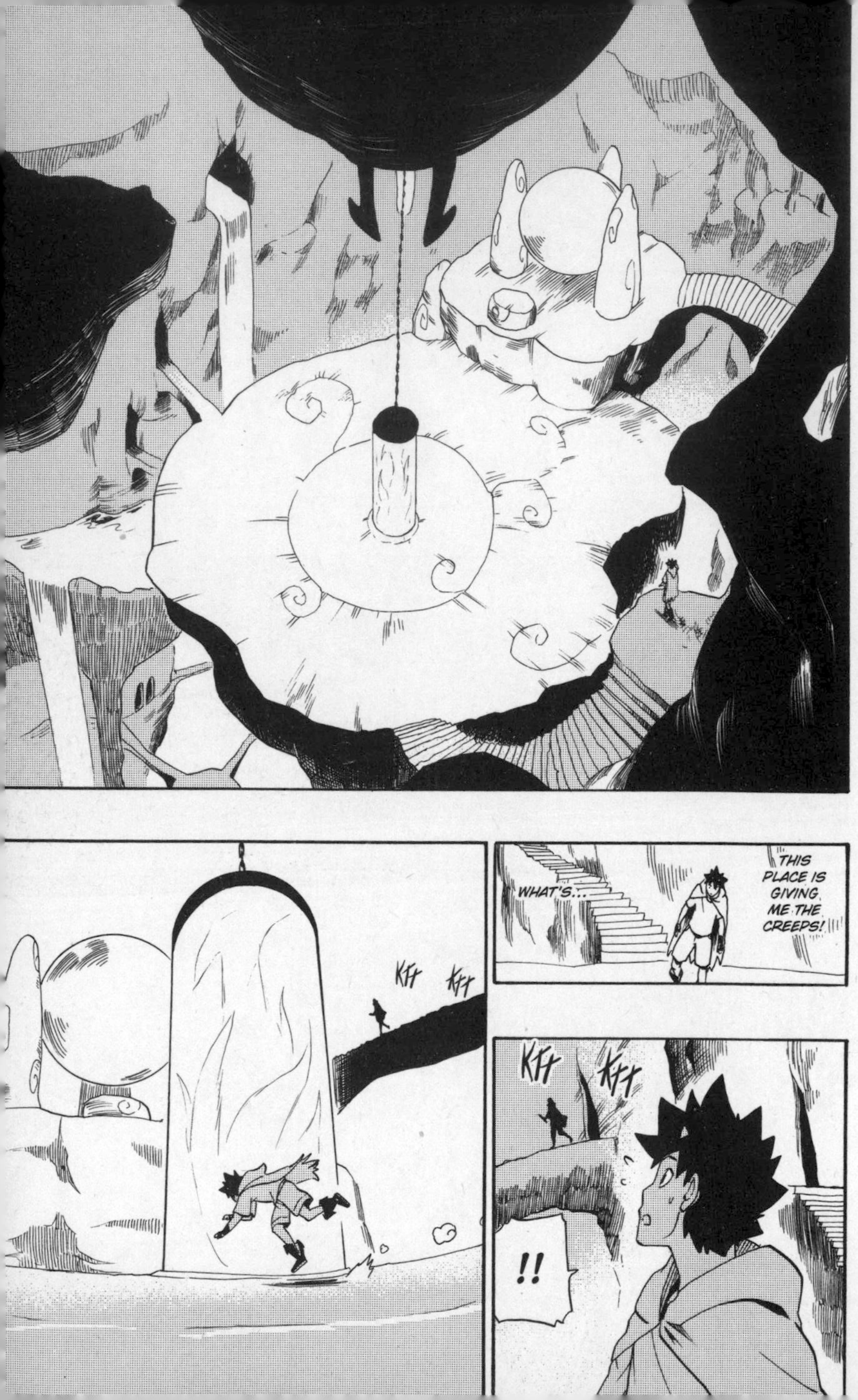

WHAT'S...

THIS PLACE IS GIVING ME THE CREEPS!

KFT KFT

KFT KFT

!!

WAIT, I'M INSIDE THE CASTLE WALLS?

AND I CAN SEE EVERYTHING GOING ON THROUGH THESE CRACKS!

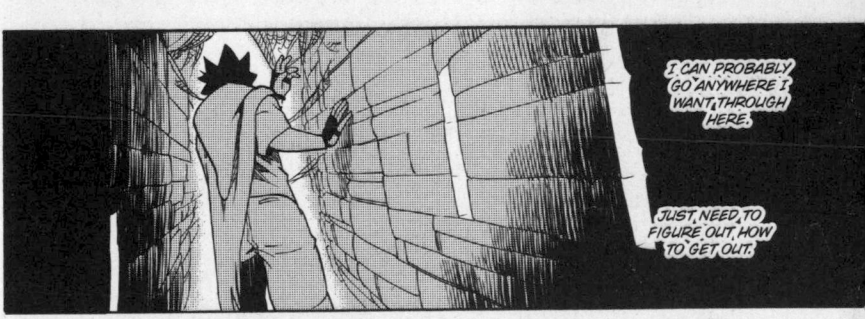

I CAN PROBABLY GO ANYWHERE I WANT THROUGH HERE.

JUST NEED TO FIGURE OUT HOW TO GET OUT.

IT'S LIKE NOBODY'S CLEANED IN THERE FOR THE PAST ONE THOUSAND YEARS OR SOMETHING!

UGH! GROSS!

IT'S DARK IN HERE SO WE PROBABLY SAW HIM GO THE WRONG WAY...

HE JUST DISAPPEARED ...?!

THAT'S IMPOSSIBLE!

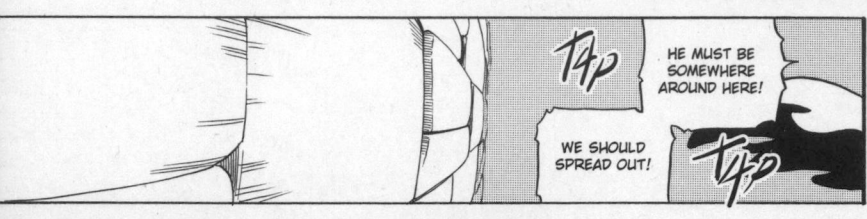

TAP

HE MUST BE SOMEWHERE AROUND HERE!

WE SHOULD SPREAD OUT!

TAP

MY ARMOR'S REALLY IN THE WAY HERE...

WUUSHH

WHO WOULD HAVE THOUGHT THERE'D REALLY BE A SECRET PASSAGE BEHIND THAT HAND SYMBOL...

BUT THEN WHAT DOES THAT MEAN ABOUT MY DREAMS?

...

!!

THAT'S THE SAME SYMBOL I SAW IN MY DREAMS!

SSSSS...

?!

LOOK! HE TURNED THAT WAY!

NOW WE'VE GOT HIM!

TAP

TAP

TAP

GOOD DAY TO YOU!

G'DAY, MY LORDS.

ANOTHER GROUP! NOW'S MY CHANCE!

SWIP

GOOD DAY!

G'DAY, MY LORD.

QUICK, I NEED TO THINK OF SOMETHING IF I DON'T WANT TO END UP THE NEXT FEW DAYS IN A CELL...

QUICK!

QUICK!

QUICK!

QUICK!

Y-YOU DON'T SAY! LET ME SEE...

!!

JUST A SECOND, MY LORD.

THERE MUST BE AN ERROR, YOUR NAME DIDN'T APPEAR WHEN YOU PASSED BY.

G'DAY, MY LORDS.

G'DAY!

I BORROWED A HOOD AND SOME ARMOR, SO THIS SHOULD WORK.

AS ALWAYS, THAT GUY NEVER LOOKS UP FROM THIS PARCHMENT...

Archives

IS EVERYTHING ALL RIGHT?

!

FWUUUUH...

SEE, THAT'S WHY I KEEP THEM ON THE SIDE. YOU SHOULD TRY IT TOO!

D'YOU SEE HOW COOL MY BANGS ARE IN FRONT OF MY EYES? I KEEP 'EM CLOSED SO I DON'T HURT MYSELF WITH THEM!

AND THERE'S OCOHO.

I WONDER WHAT THEY'RE TALKING ABOUT.

I WASN'T TRYING TO SPY ON YOU, BUT I HEARD SOME NOISE AND WANTED TO...

I'M SORRY, OCOHO.

I PROBABLY SHOULDN'T BE WATCHING THIS...

WAIT, I HEAR SOMETHING. GOTTA GO.

?

LOOK, AFTER YOU SPEND A FEW DAYS SOMEWHERE YOU QUICKLY START TO FEEL LIKE THAT. TRUST ME, YOU'RE JUST IMAGINING THINGS.

I'M SURE YOU'RE RIGHT.

AND REMEMBER THE VISIONS I WAS TALKING TO YOU ABOUT? THEY'VE BEEN GETTING CLEARER SINCE I GOT HERE.

I KEEP DREAMING ABOUT THIS SECRET PASSAGE, AND SOME OTHER STUFF.

I WON'T! BYE!

JUST DON'T DO ANYTHING YOU MIGHT REGRET LATER.

I'M INFILTRATING THE ARCHIVES!

AND WISH ME LUCK! TOMORROW, I'M STARTING MY MASTER PLAN!

?

MOLDRAID?

WHAT'S HE DOING HERE SO LATE?

HEY! I KNOW HOW TO BEHAVE MYSELF, YOU KNOW...

?!

TELL ME, WHAT'S BEEN GOING ON WITH YOU SINCE THAT GIANT NEMESIS AND THE BARONS?

DID YA CRASH INTO THE CASTLE? DESTROY AN ECOSYSTEM? TELL ME—

NOT GREAT... NONE OF THE DOCUMENTS OCOHO'S BEEN BRINGING ME ARE HELPING.

WHAT ABOUT YOUR RESEARCH? HOW'S THAT GOING?

IT'S BEEN WHAT? EIGHT DAYS? I'VE GOT SO MANY PLACES THAT HURT THAT I FEEL LIKE I'VE GOT CAVITIES IN MY ARM! IS THAT A THING?

SURE, ALONG WITH A BRAIN SPRAIN.

AND THE TRAINING! SHE JUST WON'T STOP! I'M EXHAUSTED!

AFTER THAT, NOTHING MUCH. I STILL DON'T UNDERSTAND THE SHAMANIC THINGS OCOHO'S TALKING ABOUT...

WHAT ABOUT MÉLIE AND DOC? HAVE YOU SEEN THEM SINCE?

AND THIS OTHER ONE SAYS IT'S A "HOUSE INHABITED BY A FRIENDLY SALMON..."

HUH?!

YEAH, I'M SCRATCHING THOSE FROM MY PROSPECTS LIST.

OF COURSE! IF RADIANT'S LOCATION WAS WRITTEN IN SOME BOOK, EVERYONE'D KNOW ABOUT IT!

RIGHT. IN THIS ONE CYFANDIR FAIRYTALE BOOK, THEY CALL IT THE "ISLE WITH ARDENT BOARS THAT EAT GOLDEN APPLES."

WHAT?

BUT IF YOU KEEP SCREAMING LIKE THAT I MIGHT TURN DEAF SO CALM DOWN AND GO GET ME A BLANK PIECE OF PARCHMENT!

I'M NOT BLIND, I CAN **SEE** THAT!

MISTRESS ALMA! MISTRESS ALMA!

YOUR COMMUNICATION WING'S SHINING!!

HEY, HEY!

SETH?

THANKS.

THIS IS THE SECOND FEATHER CALL YOU'VE MADE TO ME SINCE YOU ARRIVED AT THE CASTLE. WHAT'S UP?

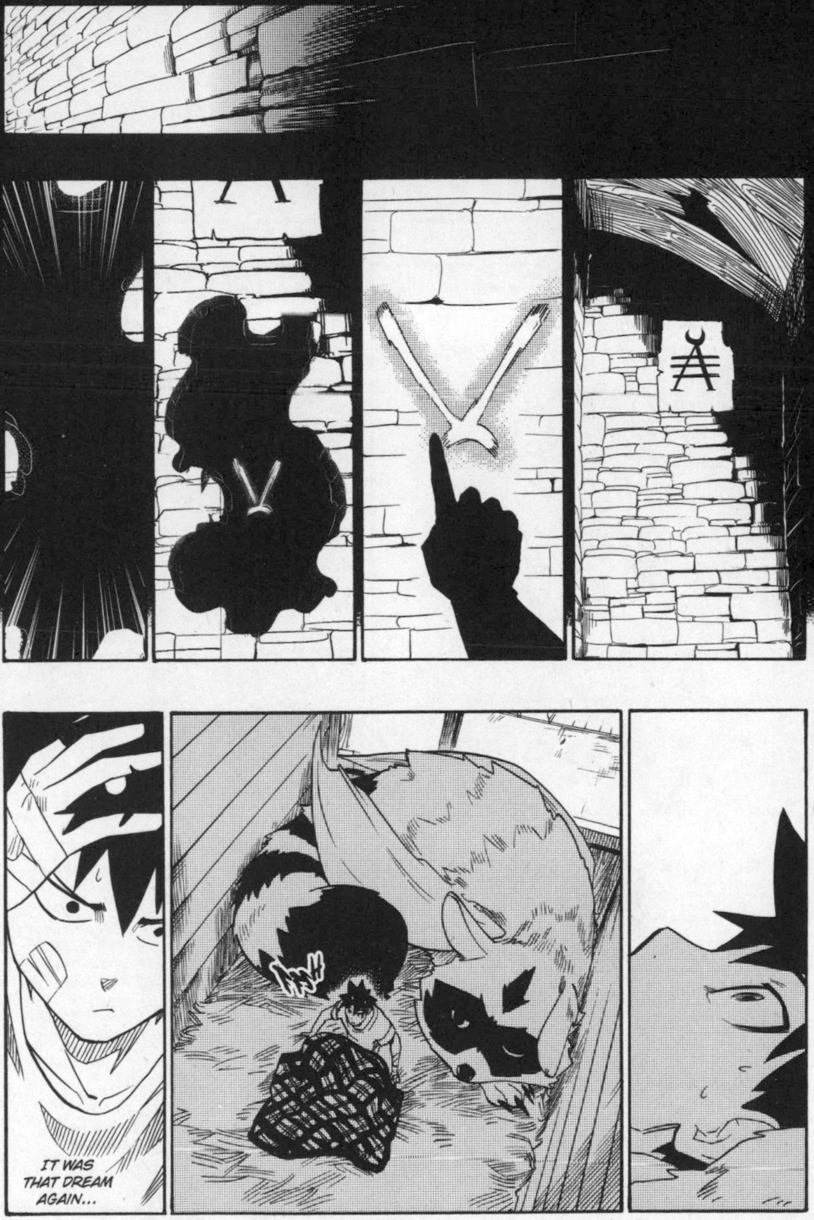

IT WAS
THAT DREAM
AGAIN...

I REALLY DOUBT THERE'S ANYTHING I CAN DO TO HELP YOU...

"YOU HAVE TROUBLE ACCEPTING HELP FROM OTHERS..."

...BUT SINCE WE BOTH NEED HELP, I GUESS IT'S WORTH A SHOT.

AND WHAT IF LORD BRANGOIRE SEES ME LOITERING AROUND HERE?

BRANGOIRE? HE DOESN'T EVEN RECOGNIZE ME AND WE SEE EACH OTHER EVERY DAY!

I DON'T HAVE A PLACE TO STAY THOUGH.

IF YOU CAN BE QUIET, THEN YOU CAN STAY HERE IN THE STABLES. BELIEVE ME WHEN I SAY DRACCOON IS A GREAT MATTRESS!

AND THEN AT NIGHT, WE'LL TRAIN UNTIL WE FALL ASLEEP!

AWESOME! THEN IT'S SETTLED! WE'LL WAKE UP AT 5 A.M. EVERY DAY AND TRAIN FOR TWO HOURS BEFORE WORK!

!!

?

AT LEAST BE MY SPARRING PARTNER! BRANGOIRE PUT ME IN THE PROTECTION TEAM, BUT THAT'S NOT ME AT ALL! I'D LOVE TO SHOW HIM, BUT...

LOOK, ARE YOU SURE? BECAUSE I DON'T KNOW WHAT YOU'RE TALKING ABOUT.

NOT JUST THAT, IT EVEN FELT LIKE I COULD FEEL EVERYTHING HAPPENING AROUND ME WITHOUT EVEN LOOKING!

LULU'S ALWAYS SLEEPING, AND I NEED TO TRAIN ON MY OWN.

A WHAT-MAN NOW?

JUST LIKE THE SHAMANS WROTE ABOUT!

I COULD HELP YOU!

I'D LOVE TO HELP, BUT I ALREADY HAVE ENOUGH THINGS TO WORRY ABOUT. I'M SORRY.

WELL, YEAH, BUT THEY LEAVE OUT A LOT OF IMPORTANT MAGIC.

COME ON!

DON'T YOU ALREADY GET TRAINING?

SO, WHAT DO YOU SAY?

YOU SAID YOU WANTED TO FIND RADIANT, RIGHT? JUST SAY THE WORD, AND I CAN BRING YOU ANYTHING YOU NEED FROM THE LIBRARIES!

OKAY, SURE, THEY'RE NOT THE ARCHIVES, BUT I'M SURE THERE'S SOMETHING OF USE TO YOU IN THERE!

Woo-

THANKS, LULLU!

?

YOU STILL OWE ME A COUPLE OF ANSWERS, WOULDN'T YOU SAY?

AND WHERE DO YOU THINK YOU'RE GOING?

YOU GOT YELLED AT BECAUSE OF ME, AND—

AH, RIGHT... SORRY FOR CAUSING YOU SO MUCH TROUBLE EARLIER. IT WASN'T ON PURPOSE...

THE AMOUNT OF FANTASIA I WAS ABLE TO DRAW FROM YOU WAS CRAZY! I JUST **NEED** TO KNOW HOW YOU DID THAT!!

AAAH! MY NECK!

THE HECK? YOUR HAIR'S IN MY EYES!

PLEASE TEACH ME!

I BARELY DID ANYTHING—THAT WAS ALL YOU!

!!

CRAAC

!!

RADIANT? WHY ARE YOU INTERESTED IN—

A DEAD-END LEAD. I CAME HERE TO TRY TO FIND WIZARD KNIGHTS LOOKING FOR RADIANT, BUT...

CHOMP

CHOMP

...APPARENTLY THE ONLY WAY TO DO THAT IS TO LOOK THROUGH THE ARCHIVES, SO...

YOU? EW!

I WOULD BUT SHE'S PISSED OFF RIGHT NOW. SHE THINKS I'VE BEEN CHEATING ON HER!

IT'S RAINING CATS AND DOGS OUT THERE! YOU CAN'T EXPECT ME TO STAY OUTSIDE?!

JUST GO BACK TO YOUR WIFE!

MYR! YOU SNEAKY LITTLE MONSTER! WHAT ARE YOU DOING IN HERE?!

FEEEHH!!

When I perceive your melons oh so round, and see you bow for something you have dropped. It makes my mood go Northbound, Of course my mood stands for my...

NOOO, NOT ANOTHER HUG!

DRACCOON! QUICK! COVER MY EARS!!

OKAY, MAYBE THERE **ARE** ONE, OR TWO, OR EVEN THREE OTHERS, BUT I'M ONLY A MAN! HOW CAN I RESIST? I EVEN MADE A NEW SONG FOR THEM!

IS SHE BLIND?

I THINK I'M GONNA JUST GO...

OH, LULU, WHAT WOULD I DO WITHOUT YOU?

ZZZZZ...

TOTALLY!

THIS HERE IS LULU. SHE'S MY SQUIRE. SHE TAKES CARE OF MY DRAGON, HELPS ME TRAIN IT—IN OTHER WORDS, SHE'S IRREPLACEABLE!

OH YEAH, LULU'S SLEEPING ON IT!

I THINK I LEFT SOME STUFF AROUND HERE.

THAT'S PERSONAL! MIND YOUR OWN BUSINESS!!

UH... YEAH.

WHAT ABOUT YOURS?

SO IS THAT HER INFECTION?

?

WHAT, SO SHOULD I WALK AROUND WITH UNDERWEAR ON MY HEAD TO HIDE MY HORNS TO FIT IN?

PERSONAL? WHAT IS IT WITH YOU GUYS HERE AND INFECTIONS! YOU CAN'T SEE THEM, YOU CAN'T TALK ABOUT THEM...

I GUESS YOU MUST HAVE COME FROM FAR AWAY IF YOU DON'T GET IT.

SO WHAT BRINGS YOU ALL THE WAY TO CAISLEAN MERLIN?

...

FEHHH!

I SAID EARS! NOT HUG!

ALL RIGHT, FORGET I ASKED!

DRACCOON! HELP! COVER MY EARS! I'VE GOT MY HANDS FULL ALREADY!

EGWIL— BREAK!

I JUST CAME TO GIVE THIS BACK TO YOU. SORRY IF I CAME AT A BAD TIME.

WHO'S THERE?

SETH? WHAT ARE YOU STILL DOING OUT IN THIS WEATHER?

THE STABLES ARE CLOSED, PLEASE COME BACK TOMORROW.

I DON'T KNOW... BECAUSE IT'S COOL?

EXACTLY! BECAUSE IT'S COLD AND TO STAY DRY! COME ON, DON'T JUST STAND THERE.

WELL, WHY DO YOU THINK WE ALL WEAR CAPES AND HOODS?

NOTHING MUCH, I WAS JUST COUNTING RAINDROPS. THIS PLACE IS CRAZY!

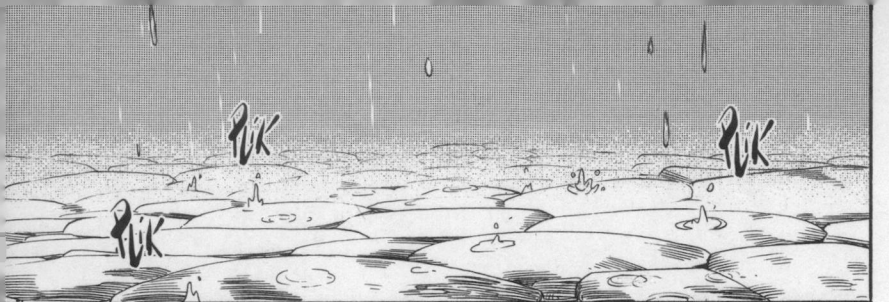

CHAPTER 36 — DREAMS

STILL?

DOES IT EVER **STOP** RAINING HERE?

AAH, AND NOW I'M COLD!

AND ME, I HAVE TROUBLE WITH PEOPLE TURNING THEIR BACKS ON ME... EVEN AFTER ALL THESE YEARS.

I AM SURE THAT DEEP DOWN, YOU ARE RIGHT, AND I AM WRONG.

YOU HAVE TROUBLE ACCEPTING HELP FROM OTHERS...

LIKE I SAID, IT'S PATHETIC.

AND I AM SURE YOU WILL DO THE SAME.

BUT I'LL LIVE, SO DON'T WORRY ABOUT ME.

BOM

POF POF

I DON'T WANT YOUR PITY.

NO, NO, SETH. PLEASE.

LOOK, MÉLIE. I...

13

HA HA... I'M SO PATHETIC...

YOU'D THINK THAT AFTER ALL THESE YEARS I'D BE OVER IT ALREADY!

I DIDN'T WANT TO GET INVOLVED, BUT THAT WAS **MEAN**, SETH!

...

WE'RE NOT KIDS, SETH.

BUT I DON'T WANT TO PUT YOU TWO IN EVEN MORE DANGER!

YES, I DO. I ALSO REMEMBER THAT WITHOUT US, THINGS WOULD HAVE GONE A LOT WORSE.

WELL, TECHNICALLY, I KIND OF AM...

ESPECIALLY NOT IF YOU THINK WE CAN'T MANAGE OURSELVES.

WE CAN'T ORDER YOU TO TAKE US WITH YOU.

...WHAT'LL HAPPEN TO YOU IF YOU'RE CLOSE TO ME?!

LOOK, WHEN I LOSE CONTROL LIKE THAT AGAIN...

DO YOU EVEN REMEMBER HOW I WAS AGAINST THE THAUMA-TURGES?

SEEING YOURSELF ACT AS IF YOU WERE SOMEONE COMPLETELY DIFFERENT AND YOU CAN'T STOP IT?!

THAT HAS NOTHING TO DO WITH IT!

DO YOU EVEN KNOW WHAT IT FEELS LIKE TO BLACK OUT AND NOT BE ABLE TO CONTROL YOURSELF?

...THAT I THOUGHT WE WERE A TEAM.

MR. SETH, YOU **DISAPPEARED**.

BEFORE YOU LEFT?

AND I'M HAVING A HARD TIME DEALING WITH THAT BECAUSE THERE WAS A TIME...

I WAS WRONG...

BUT AGAIN, YOU DO NOT NEED TO WORRY ABOUT IT...

NO, YOU'RE NOT WRONG.

I DIDN'T WANT THE TWO OF YOU TO COME ALONG.

YOU'RE RIGHT, I LEFT WITHOUT TELLING YOU TWO, AND I DID IT ON PURPOSE.

IF ANYTHING, I'M JEALOUS OF YOU.

NO, NO. IT'S NOT THAT.

THEN WHY ARE YOU SO ANGRY WITH ME?

WHY?!

IF IT'S BECAUSE I HAVEN'T REIMBURSED YOU YET FOR ALL THE MONEY FOR FOOD AND EVERYTHING, I SWEAR I—

I KNOW I MUST HAVE DONE SOMETHING WRONG!

?

NOPE.

THAT YOU'RE ABLE TO MOVE ON SO EASILY TO SOMETHING ELSE.

I DIDN'T KNOW THAT! YOU SHOULD HAVE TOLD ME BEFORE I LEFT!

...AND EVERYTHING WAS GOING GREAT! I HAD ALWAYS DREAMED OF PERFECTING MY OFFENSIVE SPELLS WITH THE WIZARD KNIGHTS! I WAS HAPPY! I WAS...

LET'S SEE... YOU ARRIVED AT THE ARTEMIS, RIGHT? AND AFTER THAT YOU LEFT FOR RUMBLE TOWN AND ALL THOSE THINGS HAPPENED...

...AND THEN YOU TALKED TO US ABOUT YOUR PLAN TO GO TO THE CASTLE FOR THAT QUEST OF YOURS...

APOLOGIZE? FOR WHAT?

?

I CAN HEAR NOISE INSIDE!

CAN YOU AT LEAST LET ME IN?

THAT'S JUST BOOBRIE FARTING IN HIS SLEEP.

SORRY, SETH, IT'S LATE AND MÉLIE'S ALREADY ASLEEP AND—

LOOK, DOC, I'D LIKE TO APOLOGIZE, BUT...

COME ON, MÉLIE. DON'T BE LIKE THAT! WE'RE FRIENDS, RIGHT?

IN THAT CASE MR. SETH, DON'T WORRY ABOUT IT.

WELL, I'M NOT ENTIRELY SURE...

?

NOPE, NOT GETTING INVOLVED HERE!

ARE WE?

WHY?

NO, GRIMM CANNOT GO BEYOND THE CASTLE WALLS.

WOULDN'T IT BE EASIER IF YOU JUST WENT TO GET IT YOURSELF? YOU SEEM TO KNOW YOUR WAY AROUND THE PLACE...

BECAUSE.

AND WHAT'S THE STONE FOR?

THINGS.

?!

BUT AFTER THAT YOU HAVE TO TELL ME WHAT YOU'RE HIDING UNDERNEATH YOUR BANDAGES—

OKAY... I'LL TRY TO HELP.

I OWE YOU AT LEAST THAT MUCH.

MAN, AT LEAST **SAY** SOMETHING BEFORE YOU LEAVE!!

GRIMM?

...

GRIMM NEEDS A CERTAIN OBJECT THAT'S IN THE CASTLE.

THEY ALLOW A USER TO RECORD ANY EVENTS THEY MAY HAVE EXPERIENCED. LIKE AN INTERACTIVE DIARY.

SOME WIZARDS HAVE A HABIT OF CARRYING AROUND GEMS AT ALL TIMES LIKE THIS ONE HERE.

THINK OF IT MORE AS A LOAN. GRIMM WOULD ONLY NEED ONE HOUR—THAT'S ALL.

?

WAIT, YOU WANT ME TO **STEAL** SOMETHING?

LOOK, GRIMM... I'M REALLY GRATEFUL FOR EVERYTHING YOU'VE DONE FOR ME, BUT...

GRIMM IS LOOKING FOR ONE OWNED BY A CERTAIN WIZARD NAMED MAGOSIA.

ALONGSIDE THE CASTLE ARCHIVES, THERE IS ALSO THE **ANMATHECARY**—A COLLECTION OF GEMS THAT USED TO BE OWNED BY GREAT WIZARDS FROM THE PAST.

NEVERTHELESS, YOU WERE ABLE TO INFILTRATE THE CASTLE AND GET YOURSELF INTO AN ADVANTAGEOUS POSITION!

THEY MUST HAVE **SOME** INFORMATION IN THE ARCHIVES, BUT THEY KICKED ME OUT SO THERE'S NO WAY FOR ME TO CHECK IT OUT.

I ALSO SAW MÉLIE AND DOC, BUT THEY SEEMED ANGRY WITH ME...

I GUESS...

TRY THE LUCHORPAN INN, IF IT STILL EXISTS. THE OTHER INNS ARE PROBABLY TOO EXPENSIVE FOR THEM.

MÉLIE AND DOC, AT CAISLEAN MERLIN?

YEAH, BUT I HAVE NO IDEA WHERE THEY ARE NOW.

YOU NEVER WERE A WIZARD KNIGHT. AND YOU LIKE TO AIR OUT YOUR ARMPITS IN A WIDE-OPEN FIELD.

BEFORE YOU KNOW IT, I'LL BE ABLE TO WRITE A BIOGRAPHY ABOUT YOU!

OKAY.

SO THAT'S IT? JUST NO?

WELL, NOW I KNOW TWO THINGS ABOUT YOU.

NO.

THANKS.

BUT HOW DO YOU KNOW ALL THIS?

WERE YOU A WIZARD KNIGHT YOURSELF?

HOW DO YOU DO IT ANYWAY? YOU JUST GO ALONG YOUR WAY WITHOUT ANYONE NOTICING YOU.

MAYBE I SHOULD JUST STAND HERE TOO AND WAIT FOR RADIANT TO FALL ON MY HEAD.

PERHAPS GRIMM SHOULD JUST DEPLOY AN ASTRONOMIC AMOUNT OF FANTASIA INSTEAD?

PFFT... NO...

YOU AIRING OUT YOUR ARMPITS IN IN A FLOWER FIELD NOW?

NOT EXACTLY VERY DISCREET.

IS THAT YOUR GOAL AS WELL?

AND IT ALSO KEEPS GRIMM AWAY FROM THE WORLD.

IT'S TRUE THAT GRIMM CAN EASILY KEEP UNDESIRABLE ATTENTION OFF OF HIM.

PLAYING A SCARECROW IN A FIELD, A ZOMBIE IN A CEMETERY, A LEPER ON THE SIDE OF THE ROAD...

OH YES, MY QUEEN!
AND THAT HE WILL ONCE AGAIN BE WORTHY IN THE EYES OF MERLIN!
LET'S HOPE OUR FARMER FRIEND WILL KNOW HOW TO UTILIZE THIS NEW LEASE ON HIS FIELD THAT YOU SO BRAVELY PROTECTED.
I MUST NOW GO BACK TO MY ROYAL AFFAIRS. BUT 'TWAS A FRUITFUL VISIT. CONGRATULATIONS ON YOUR WORK WITH THESE FINE NEW RECRUITS.
PWUUU
OH, YOUR MAJESTY IS TOO KIND. THANK YOU SO MUCH!
I KNOW, AREN'T I? BUT NO NEED TO FLATTER ME SO MUCH, MY LORD!
OH, NO! I DIDN'T MEAN TO...
SHHHH
...
!!
WHAT'RE YOU STILL DOING OGLING THE QUEEN! GO BACK TO THE CASTLE!

BUT WHY? ARE WE WORTHY OF BEING HIS SUCCESSORS? OF HIS WARD?

YOU MUST LISTEN WHEN THE EARTHLY SPIRITS AWAKEN!

ARE WE WORTHY OF THE LAND OF CYFANDIR, WHICH HE LOVED SO MUCH AND DEFENDED WITH SUCH FERVOR AGAINST THE BARBARIC INVADERS?

MERLIN'S SPIRIT IS AGITATED. I CAN FEEL IT IN MY BONES!

WE ALL MUST ASK OURSELVES THESE QUESTIONS.

STHHAA...

MY QUEEN!

YOUR BEHAVIOR COULD'VE HAD GRAVE CONSEQUENCES....

...BUT YOU HAD NOBLE INTENTIONS, WORTHY OF MERLIN'S LEGACY, OCOHO.

SO NO NEED TO GET ALL WORKED UP!

AND WOULD YOU PLEASE STOP LOOKING UP MY SKIRT...

!!

OH, BRANGOIRE, I CAME HERE ON A WHIM. NOTHING MORE!

YOUR HIGHNESS! I DIDN'T KNOW YOU WOULD HONOR US WITH YOUR PRESENCE! IF I HAD, WE WOULD HAVE—

SHE'S HUGE! I GUESS THAT MUST BE HER INFECTION...

...AND WHEN MY PEOPLE SUFFER, I SUFFER!

I WAS INTERESTED IN SEEING ONE OF THOSE SPECTRUMS UP CLOSE MYSELF.

THOSE BEINGS ARE TORMENTING MY PEOPLE...

PEOPLE SAY THEY APPEAR TO PEOPLE WHO DEAL WITH FOREIGNERS... EVEN IF IT'S ALL LEGAL! WE'RE NOTHING BUT HONEST FARMERS, MY QUEEN, BUT WHY DO WE ATTRACT EVIL?!

YOUR MAJESTY, WE'RE ALL SCARED! THESE SPECTRUMS AND THESE APPARITIONS AT NIGHT—WE SAW A DULLAHAN HERE! A FAIRY THAT CARRIES ITS OWN HEAD!

BOW DOWN A LITTLE LOWER.

OH!

OH, MY QUEEN, THANK YOU FOR YOUR SYMPATHY! WITHOUT YOUR KNIGHTS THERE WOULDN'T BE ANYTHING LEFT OF OUR FIELDS!

GLAD TO HEAR.

QUEEN BOADICÉE
-QUEEN OF CYFANDIR-

THE REST OF YOU ARE BIG, FAT ZEROS! WHAT WERE YOU THINKING BREAKING THE FORMATION OF THE CONFINEMENT SPELL AND STOPPING TO ATTACK, HUH?!

ACTUALLY, I AM ONLY TALKING ABOUT MORDRED AND SAGRAMOR!!

FIRST OF ALL, IT PUTS EVERYONE IN DANGER!

AND SECONDLY! UH...

IT, UH... FWSHFBL FLABLUUBLU...

AND DON'T MAKE ME REPEAT MYSELF!!

ON THE GROUND? I DIDN'T ORDER ANYONE TO BE ON THE GROUND!! WHY DID YOU DO THAT?!

ANSWER ME!!

IT FELT LIKE IT CAME FROM OCOHO'S SPELL ON THE GROUND!

LORD BRANGOIRE, IF I MAY? WE DIDN'T HAVE ENOUGH FANTASIA LEFT.

I'M OCOHO...

NO. I, UH...

!!

YEAH, I FELT THE SAME THING.

CHAPTER 35

THE WIZARD QUEEN

CONGRAT-ULATIONS. ANOTHER SPECTRUM NEMESIS VANQUISHED!

CRUNCH

SORRY, WHEN I SAY "ALL"...

...THAT DOESN'T INCLUDE SOME OF YOU.

I AM CERTAIN THAT YOU ALL WILL MAKE AMAZING WIZARD KNIGHTS SOME DAY!

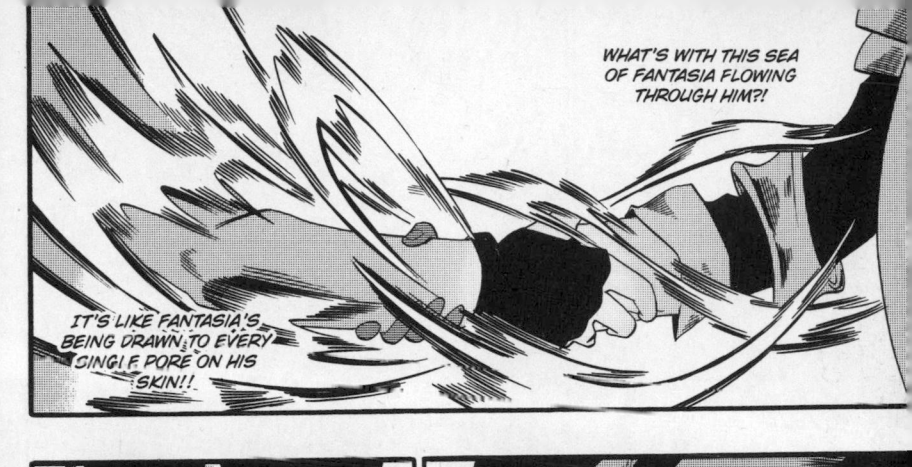

WHAT'S WITH THIS SEA OF FANTASIA FLOWING THROUGH HIM?!

IT'S LIKE FANTASIA'S BEING DRAWN TO EVERY SINGLE PORE ON HIS SKIN!!

IT'S DISINTEGRATING!

IF WE DON'T ACT NOW...

...

WE'VE LOST CONTACT! IT SEEMS THAT THE DOME BELOW IS SIPHONING ENORMOUS QUANTITIES OF FANTASIA!

MORDRED! THE NEMESIS!!

MIGHT AS WELL AIM STRAIGHT FOR THE FARMERS TOO! THEY'RE GOING TO END UP STARVING TO DEATH AT THIS RATE, BUT I GUESS IT'S ALL OKAY SO LONG AS THE NEMESIS IS GONE, RIGHT?!

THEN WHAT **ARE** YOUR ORDERS? JUST KEEP FIRING UNTIL THERE'S NOTHING LEFT?

YOU CAN DO THAT?

YEAH, BUT THOSE AREN'T MY ORDERS!

ELIMINATE THE NEMESIS!

WHAT DO YOU NEED ME TO DO?

I'LL DO THE INCANTATION, BUT TO MAKE SURE THE SPELL RANGE EXTENDS AS FAR AS POSSIBLE, I'LL NEED YOU TO ACCUMULATE AS MUCH FANTASIA AS POSSIBLE.

IT'S SLOWING DOWN. LET'S GO!

WAIT!

ALL RIGHT, I'LL DO IT. BUT I NEED YOUR HELP.

I'M GOING BACK.

FOOSHH

THERE WERE ALL THOSE SIGNS! NIGHTLY APPARITIONS! BUT *NOOO*, YOU JUST HAD TO DO WHAT **YOU** WANTED!!

DIDN'T I TELL YOU THIS'D HAPPEN IF YOU HUNG AROUND WITH THOSE STRANGERS!!

I'M SORRY, I–

M'FIELDS!

NOOO !

IT'S YOUR FAULT IF THEY DESTROY EVERYTHING!

THEY'RE WEAKENING THE NEMESIS BEFORE THE FINAL ATTACK.

NOTHING'S HITTING! THEY'RE JUST DESTROYING EVERYTHING AROUND IT!

WE CAN'T JUST STAND AROUND AND DO **NOTHING**!!

WHERE ARE YOU... *?!*

VOOF FT

SO AFTER ABOUT 15 OR 16 TIMES...OR MAYBE IT WAS–

I SAW IT TOO! I WAS TILLING MA FARM, MINDING MY OWN BUSINESS, I LOOK DOWN, LOOK BACK UP, BACK DOWN, LOOK BACK UP, DOWN, UP...

SO AFTER THAT??

CAN YOU JUST GET TO THE ACTUAL "BAM-MING!"

AFTER THAT, "BAM"! AND THEN WE ALL CAME 'ERE TO HIDE!

...

SPOO

GPOK

UM... YEAH.

OH GOOD! YOU'RE SAFE!

DANGER TO THE LEFT? WOOPS, PULL TO THE LEFT! DANGER IN FRONT OF YOU? THERE! YOU JUST PULLED UP! IT'S A DRAGON, NOT A WAGON!!

THAT'S WHY I ASKED YOU TO HOLD THE REINS! DANGER TO THE RIGHT? WOOPS, PULL TO THE RIGHT!

VSHH

WE WERE GOING TO GET HIT!!

WHAT WERE YOU THINKING TRYING TO BLOCK AN ATTACK WITH YOUR BARE HANDS?! WHY NOT SPIT ON A FIRE WHILE YOU'RE AT IT?!

CRR

KLK

"HIDE YOUR HORNS."

"KEEP A LOW PROFILE."

AAH! MY HOOD!

THEY'RE CALLED WIZARD KNIGHTS, CHILDREN!

NO, LOOK! HE'S GOT LITTLE HORNS!

MOMMY! LOOK, THERE'S A COW KNIGHT THAT FELL FROM THE SKY!

MOOO! MOOO!

YOU SURE IT WASN'T MORE LIKE "PSSSH! BOOM," LIKE SOMETHING FALLING FROM THE SKY?

WHAT DO YOU MEAN, "BAM! JUST LIKE THAT?"

NO, NO! IT WAS "BAM!" LIKE SOMETHING APPEARING OUT OF THIN AIR!

POC

OF COURSE WE CAN! I WAS THE ONE WHO FOUND IT BEFORE Y'ALL CAME IN! BAM! JUST LIKE THAT!

NO, NO, NO! THESE ARE JUST WHITE HAIRS!

AND WHAT ARE YOU EVEN DOING HERE? CAN'T YOU SEE THAT GINORMOUS NEMESIS THERE?

WOOO

OSHA

BZZZ

SHIN

PHEW, THAT WAS CLOSE!

HFF!

HFF!

AT LEAST I'M LUCKY MY OTHER ARM SEEMS UNAFFECTED!

BUT MY LEFT ARM ISN'T SENSING FANTASIA ANYMORE! MUST BE BECAUSE OF TORQUE'S SWORD. GRIMM WAS RIGHT...

DOESN'T SEEM LIKE THAT DID ANYTHING...

...

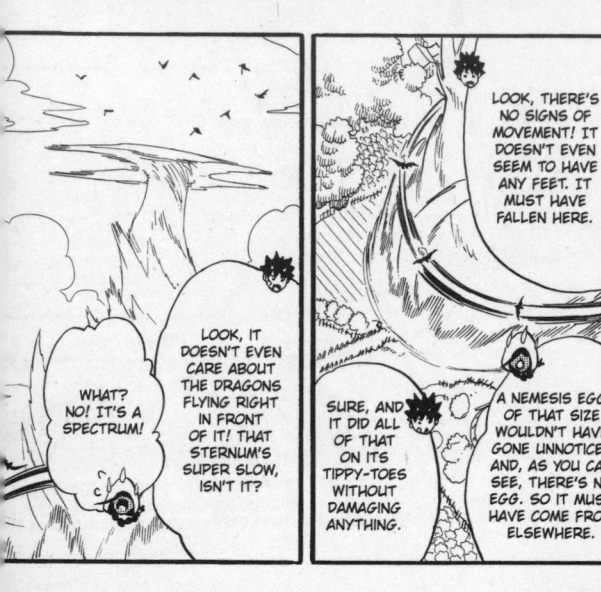

WHAT? NO! IT'S A SPECTRUM!

LOOK, IT DOESN'T EVEN CARE ABOUT THE DRAGONS FLYING RIGHT IN FRONT OF IT! THAT STERNUM'S SUPER SLOW, ISN'T IT?

LOOK, THERE'S NO SIGNS OF MOVEMENT! IT DOESN'T EVEN SEEM TO HAVE ANY FEET. IT MUST HAVE FALLEN HERE.

SURE, AND IT DID ALL OF THAT ON ITS TIPPY-TOES WITHOUT DAMAGING ANYTHING.

A NEMESIS EGG OF THAT SIZE WOULDN'T HAVE GONE UNNOTICED AND, AS YOU CAN SEE, THERE'S NO EGG. SO IT MUST HAVE COME FROM ELSEWHERE.

IT'LL STOP IT FROM MOVING WHEN WE GO ON THE OFFENSIVE.

SETH, I'M TRYING TO CONCENTRATE HERE!

IT WAS ALREADY NOT MOVING—LOOK AROUND IT!

SERIOUSLY, SETH! SHUT UP!

I ALREADY HAVE ENOUGH TROUBLE WITH THE GYSONI, BUT NOW I CAN BARELY FEEL LORD BRANGOIRE!

OF COURSE, IF WE KEEP HANGING AROUND SO CLOSE TO IT, SOMETHING IS BOUND TO HAPPEN!

SURE, SPECTER! BESIDES BUMPING INTO HIM, I PERSONALLY DON'T SEE THE DANGER.

THE FIRST SPECTER APPEARED HERE NOT TOO LONG AGO, FOLLOWED BY MANY OTHERS.

YES. ALL ATTACKS GO RIGHT THROUGH THEM!

A SPECTRUM NEMESIS?

SO THERE'S REALLY NOTHING WE CAN DO AGAINST THEM?

THE ONLY THING WE CAN DO IS CONFINE THEM WITHIN A RESTRICTED AREA TO MITIGATE FURTHER DAMAGE...

I DON'T KNOW...

YOU MEAN THOSE TWO FAMOUS NEWBIES?

SO EVEN REAL KNIGHTS CAN'T STOP THEM?

...BUT UP UNTIL NOW, ONLY MORDRED AND SAGRAMOR HAVE SUCCEEDED IN THAT!

CHAPTER 34

SPECTRUM NEMESIS

YES, I AM! BUT YOU HAVE TO HOLD THE REINS!

WHAT ARE YOU DOING HERE IF YOU CAN'T FLY A DRAGON!?

BUT THAT'S WHY YOU'RE HERE! TO STEER DRACCOON!!

I MEAN, NOT OFTEN... LIKE, ONCE OR TWICE...

WAIT, I THOUGHT WE WERE GOING TO FIGHT A NEMESIS!

MYR!!

I WAS TALKING TO THIS OLD SMELLY GUY, AND AFTER THAT EVERYTHING JUST KIND OF HAPPENED.

I DUNNO!

IT ALL JUST WENT BY SO QUICKLY!

EVERYTHING OKAY, OCOHO?

EVERYTHING'S FINE! I WAS JUST CONCENTRATING A BIT!!

HOW AM I GOING TO DISTINGUISH MYSELF LIKE THIS?

THIS CANNOT BE HAPPENING!!

AT THIS RATE I WON'T EVER BE INDUCTED INTO THE ORDER!!

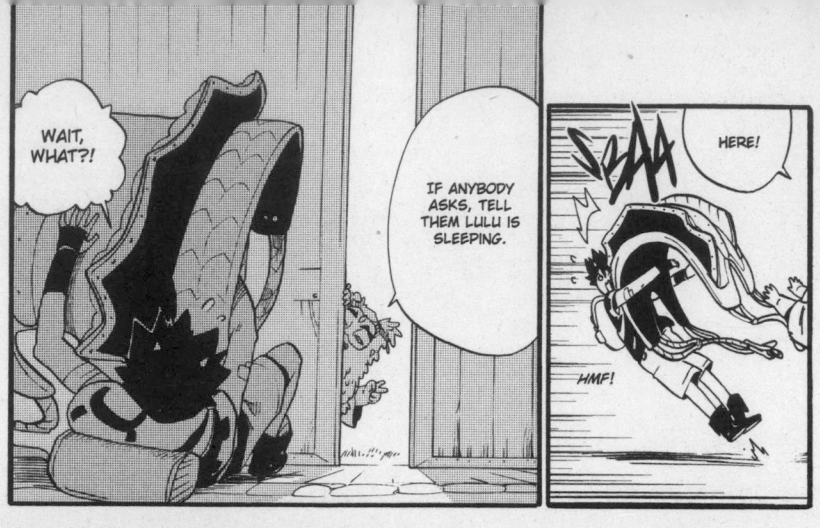

WAIT, WHAT?!

IF ANYBODY ASKS, TELL THEM LULU IS SLEEPING.

HERE!

HMF!

BOM

KLOP KLOK

WAIT, WHY AM I EVEN FOLLOWING THIS NUTJOB?!

I'D BETTER PUT THIS DOWN AND RUN AWAY BEFORE...

OKAY, THEY'RE NOT AFTER US. YOU CAN TAKE A BREAK NOW. I JUST SAVED YOUR BUTT!

D-DID WE REALLY NEED TO CLIMB ALL THE WAY UP HERE?!

HUFF! HUFF!

HEY! YOU'RE THE REASON WE GOT INTO TROUBLE IN THE FIRST—

WHAT THE HECK IS HE DOING PLAYING AROUND WITH A TRUMPET LIKE THAT ON A ROOFTOP?!

BWUUUUUUUUUUUUU

WHAT?! BUT...

THAT'S NO TRUMPET, IT'S A HORN! HURRY, INSIDE!

OH!

SCIATH— SHIELD!!

HMM!!

OH NO! I CAN EVEN SOMEHOW TASTE IT!

I'M EVEN FEELING IT THROUGH MY EYES! BLARG...

AAAH! THIS SMELL!! HE'S SENDING HIS STENCH OUR WAY!!!

MY SHIELD ISN'T STOPPING IT—

?

FWUSH!!

FWUSH!!

MYYYYR !!!

MYR!

MY EYES ARE DRYING OUT!!

M-MY GUMS ARE RETRACTING! AND MY TEETH ARE FALLING OUT! AAAAARGH!!

HM, LOOKS LIKE YOU DIDN'T GET WHAT I WAS SAYING.

For his horse he held a fixation,
Grown stronger through their relation,
And many had seen it, but word was mum,
Gontar with a finger up her ...

DUDE! KEEP IT DOWN!!

HOW IS THAT A **VALUABLE** PIECE OF ADVICE?!

WELL, LOOK WHO'S A GENIUS NOW! HERE, HOLD THIS FOR A SEC.

SO YOU'RE SAYING I SHOULD GO TO THE STABLES!

BUT THAT'S NOT GOING TO HELP GET ME INTO THE ARCHIVES.

Blah blah blah might,
Blah blah blah knight,
Blah blah in their stables,
come on,
Blah blah blah you moron!

OOOH!

Every good knight daily should ensure their horse's stall is clean of manure, for it to feel all right.

HM... STILL NOTHING...

WHA...?

...BUT THE INSIDE OF THE CASTLE? THERE'S NO PATCH OF GRASS TO TOUCH OR INCH OF DIRT TO STAND ON!

THE STABLES, THAT'S ONE THING...

YOU'RE ON YOUR OWN FOR THAT! I NEVER SET FOOT IN THOSE STONE MONSTROSITIES!

YOU'RE AN IMP?

WHO ARE YOU?

...

I WASN'T TALKING TO YOU.

TOTALLY.

THE IMP STATUE.

IF YOU DON'T WANT ANY ANSWERS, THEN DON'T ASK ANY QUESTIONS.

ALL RIGHT, THEN. YOUR CHOICE! BUT I'VE SPENT A LOT OF TIME HERE SO I KNOW A THING OR TWO ABOUT LOITERING INCOGNITO.

HEH HEH HEH, YOU'VE CAUGHT ME! BUT THAT DOESN'T MAKE MY ADVICE ANY LESS VALUABLE.

HONESTLY, I CAN DO WITHOUT GETTING ADVICE FROM A MAN WITH UNDERWEAR IN HIS BEARD...

SURE YOU ARE.

Closer to a knight there is none,
than a horse, in the long run,
'twas a tale that is quite bizarre,
Of young paladin Gontar.

THEN LISTEN TO THIS!

OKAY... I'M LISTENING.

HM! HM!

JUST BE A KID.

THEN, HOW?!

SURE, THERE ARE A FEW INFECTED ADMITTED INTO THE RANKS, DEPENDING ON ONE'S INFECTION. SOME CAN PRETEND NOTHING'S WRONG UNTIL THE ACCOLADE. OTHERS CAN'T.

GUARDS. FRAUD.

FWUSHH

WELL, I GUESS THAT'S A DEAD END...

Castle Registrar

BOOM

I THINK.

I VAGUELY REMEMBER HEARING ABOUT IT.

EITHER THAT OR IT WAS SOMETHING ELSE.

OH, OF COURSE THERE WAS A TIME WHEN THE ORDER OF MERLIN WAS LOOKING FOR RADIANT...

WELL, ALL THE FORCES ARE TASKED TO OBSERVE NEMESES DROPS IN CYFANDIR AND NEARBY ALLIED ISLETS.

NOWADAYS, HOWEVER? NOTHING!

BUT THIS WAS MY ONLY LEAD!

THEN AGAIN, IT'S MY ONLY LEAD...

AFTER THE ARTEMIS INSTITUTE STUFF, I CAN'T AFFORD GETTING MYSELF DRAFTED HERE TOO!

IF THERE ARE, MAYBE THEY'D BE IN THE ARCHIVES.

ARE YOU SURE THERE'S NOTHING LEFT? NO NOTES OR ANYTHING?

ACCESS TO THE ARCHIVES IS RESTRICTED TO MEMBERS OF THE ORDER!

ALL RIGHT! WHERE CAN I FIND THEM?

CRAP!

CHAPTER 33

THE STATUE IMP

BUT ONE MYSTERY AT A TIME I GUESS.

I DON'T GET IT...

...AND SHE DIDN'T SEEM TO BE HAVING A FIT, EITHER.

MÉLIE'S USUALLY NOT CLOSED OFF LIKE THAT...

W...

WHAAAT ?!

RADIANT?

Castle Registrar

OH, IT'S BEEN AGES SINCE ANYONE AROUND HERE'S SHOWN AN INTEREST IN THAT!

YES, MA'AM!

HUH...?

HELLO, SETH.

COME NOW, MR. DOC. WE HAVE WORK TO DO.

HOW DID THAT HAPPEN? WHAT ARE YOU...

DOC! DID YOU GROW?!

HEY! MÉLIE!

HEY...

IT'S ME! SETH!

HOW WOULD I KNOW? THAT'S JUST WHAT PEOPLE CALL THEM.

NIGHTMARES? WAIT, DO NEMESES SLEEP?!

THEY'RE AT THE TOP OF THEIR CLASS! THEY KEEP RACKING UP BIG VICTORIES ONE AFTER THE OTHER! THEY'RE THE "NEMESES' WORST NIGHTMARE!"

WELL, MERLIN DID LIVE CENTURIES AGO, SO HIS MAGIC MUST HAVE BEEN PRETTY PRIMITIVE! I'M SURE THEY'RE ALREADY BETTER THAN HIM!

SOME SAY THEY MIGHT EVEN SURPASS MERLIN HIMSELF SOMEDAY!

MAKES SENSE, YES!

YOU KNOW, THEIR INDUCTION TO THE ORDER OF MERLIN?

ORDER OF MER-WHO??

THE ORDER OF MERLIN! OF THE WIZARD KNIGHTS! HOW DO YOU NOT KNOW THIS?!

ACCO-WHAT NOW?

THEY'RE STILL YOUNG, BUT PEOPLE ARE SAYING THOSE TWO MIGHT EVEN BECOME THE HEAD LORDS AT THEIR ACCOLADE.

THAT'D MAKE THEM THE YOUNGEST HEAD LORDS EVER!

CAN YOU BELIEVE THE LACK OF CULTURE!

TOTALLY!

PSH, COME, LET'S NOT WASTE ANY MORE TIME TALKING TO A HICK LIKE HIM.

WELL, YEAH. THEY'RE NOT REAL ONES YET, RIGHT? I DIDN'T COME ALL THE WAY TO SEE THEM...

OKAY, BUT THEN WHERE ARE THE REAL WIZARD KNIGHTS?

WHAT DID YOU JUST SAY?!

THEY'RE COMING!

LOOK, THERE THEY ARE!

AND, EVERYONE SEEMS TO BE GOING ON JUST FINE.

LOOKS LIKE THIS PLACE BOTH HAS INFECTED AND NON-INFECTED PEOPLE LIVING TOGETHER.

-CAISLEAN MERLIN-
CASTLE OF THE WIZARD KNIGHTS

BARONESS ALKON, DID WE NOT SPEND COUNTLESS HOURS TALKING ABOUT RUMBLE TOWN WITHOUT EVER SETTING FOOT IN ITS LANDS?

AND WHAT DID THAT DO FOR US, *HM*?

PERHAPS, BUT BEFORE LONG WE WILL ALL FEEL THE EFFECTS OF THE REDUCED PRODUCTION.

SURELY WE COULD HAVE TALKED ABOUT THIS AT HOME, BARON DOUSSANT.

WE **MUST** ANTICIPATE THE NEXT CRISIS BEFORE IT HITS. THE BACKGROUND, ONGOING TENSIONS, OBSTACLES AND OPPORTUNITIES... IT IS UP TO US TO FIND HOW WE CAN BE THE CATALYST THAT WILL TIP THOSE SCALES IN OUR FAVOR.

FIND?! I CAN FIND **ANYTHING!**

IS THE RUMBLE TOWN CRISIS REALLY AN EVENT MERELY CAUSED BY A COUPLE OF WIZARDS?

...AND RESULTING IN THE STOPPING OF OUR FACTORIES, A DIVE IN OUR PROFITS AND THE WEAKENING OF OUR FORTUNE AND PRIVILEGES.

NO, OF COURSE NOT. THOSE WIZARDS WERE MERELY THE CATALYST THAT STARTED THE CHAIN OF EVENTS THAT WOULD LATER UNFOLD ON THAT ISLET, TURNING EVERYTHING UPSIDE DOWN...

AND AS EVERYBODY KNOWS, WHEN IT COMES TO CLOTHING A PERSON, THERE IS NO ONE BETTER SUITED THAN ME, BARON FURGONDE!

PERFECTLY!

LET ME ASK YOU THIS, MY FRIEND... HOW IS YOUR TEXTILE COMPANY WORKING FOR YOU?

AND I STILL DO NOT UNDERSTAND WHY WE HAVE COME ALL THE WAY HERE. THE WIZARD KNIGHTS HAVE NEVER SHOWN ANY INTEREST IN RELINQUISHING THESE LANDS!

HOW ABOUT **UNCLOTHING** SOMEONE FOR A CHANGE....

WHAT'S THAT, DEAR?

SHUSH, PLEASE! JUST HEARING ABOUT IT MAKES ME LOSE MY APPETITE!

NOT TO MENTION THE PRICES OF METAL FOR PAZZ AND HIS COIN MINTING.

YEAH!

THAT MAY BE TRUE, BUT I HAVE ALSO HEARD THAT YOUR DYE PRICES HAVE BEEN INCREASING...

AS HAVE WOOD PRICES FOR CRISTOLOM'S BUSINESS.

GNF...!

WHAT'S GOTTEN INTO YOU? ON TOP OF OUR USUAL VENTURES, WE STILL HAVE PLENTY OF WEAPONS STOCKS THAT WE SELL AT HIGH PRICES TO THE INQUISITION.

AND NOW WE ALSO HAVE TO DEAL WITH DELAYS IN PRODUCTION FROM OUR FACTORIES IN RUMBLE TOWN.

A pebble.

A PEBBLE.

SCRIT SCRIT

Solember 21,

Day 18 of our voyage.

We berthed this morning at an unknown land, greeted by an apocalyptic downpour. I thus christened this land Cristolombia.

PAZZ, DON'T START! YOU...

YOU COULD HAVE AT LEAST CAPTURED THOSE GHOSTS TO HELP ME GET OVER THIS PAIN.

HOW DARE YOU HAVE FUN WITH YOUR ROCK EVEN AFTER LETTING MY GOATMAN ESCAPE?!

Pazz, don't start! You...

NO, NO, NO! DON'T WRITE THAT DOWN...

No, no, no! Don't write that down...

THIS ISLET ALREADY HAS A NAME, BARON CRISTOLOM.

Be quiet!

I uncovered a peculiar artifact that had been unsoiled by eyes for the past thousands—no, billions of years. 'Tis a truly fascinating piece containing ancient knowledge thought lost throughout the ages. A piece which we civilized people call...

I VOTE WE LEAVE AND GO BACK TO OUR EASTERN STATES! LESS RAIN, LESS GHOSTS...

GOODNESS!

THANKS.

THE CASTLE? WAIT, HOW'D YOU KNOW THAT'S WHERE I WAS GOING? I DIDN'T NOTICE YOU FOLLOWING ME!

VERY MUCH SEPARATED FROM THE MAIN ROADS AND ABOUT HALF A DAY ON FOOT FROM THE WIZARD KNIGHTS' CASTLE.

ACHOO! SNIFF!

IT'S FREEZING HERE... WHERE ARE WE ANYWAY?

AND YOU ALSO DID NOT NOTICE THAT AIRSHIP HEADED STRAIGHT FOR YOU EITHER.

AND WHY DID YOU NOT TELL **THEM** YOU WERE LEAVING?

POINT TAKEN...

BUT WHY DIDN'T YOU TELL US WHERE YOU WERE GOING? WE COULD'VE—

MÉLIE AND DOC.

...

YOU AND GRIMM BOTH.

...I DIDN'T WANT TO DRAG THEM ALL INTO THIS.

IT'S JUST THAT...

NEVERTHELESS, YOU SHOULD HAVE WHAT IT TAKES TO BE ABLE TO FINISH A FIGHT. YOU HESITATE FOR TOO LONG ON WHETHER OR NOT TO USE FANTASIA AND **THAT** COULD HAVE COST YOU DEARLY.

YOU KNOW, SO I DON'T END UP NEEDING TO RECOVER FROM HOLES IN MY BODY EVERY WEEK.

GUESS I SHOULD LEARN TO DO THAT.

WISE DECISION!

AND INCITING FEAR IS ONE OF GRIMM'S MUCH-LOVED TACTICS.

THERE ARE MANY WAYS TO DEAL WITH THREATS WITHOUT SPILLING BLOOD.

LAST TIME, IT COULD HAVE COST A LOT OF LIVES.

NOT REALLY KEEN ON MAKING THAT HAPPEN AGAIN.

WELCOME BACK TO THE WORLD OF THE LIVING.

IF YOU ARE TALKING ABOUT THE MERCHANT BARONS, THEN YES.

YOU BEAT THEM ALL BY YOURSELF?

WHAT ARE YOU— WAIT, DID YOU SAVE ME FROM THOSE OLD DANCING WEIRDOS?

GRIMM?

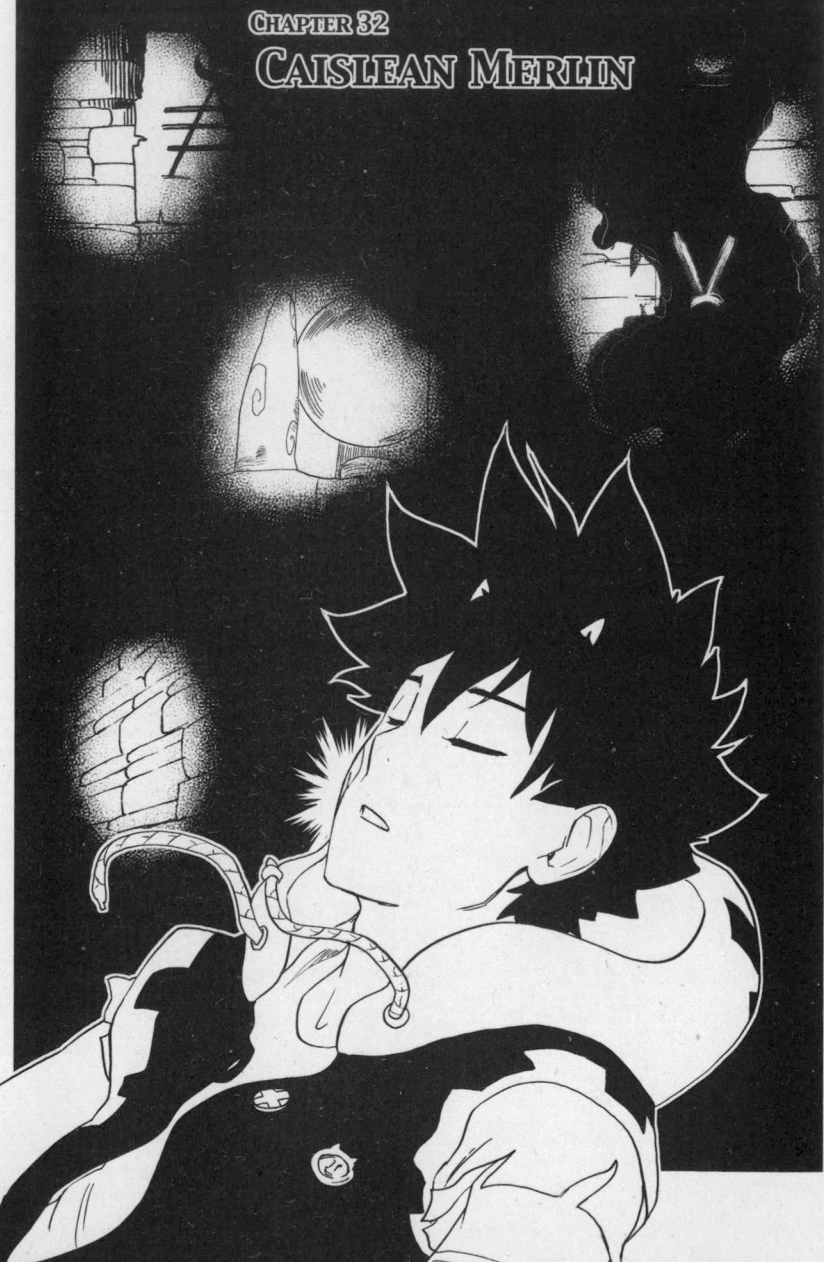
CHAPTER 32
CAISLEAN MERLIN

IT'S USELESS HIDING FROM ME BECAUSE I **WILL** FIND YOU! I CAN FIND ANYTHING! I'M THE GREATEST FINDER OF OUR AGE!

STRANGE, THIS IS WHERE HE SHOULD HAVE LANDED...

FSH

AHA! THERE YOU ARE!! GET OUT OF THERE AND FACE ME LIKE A MAN!

THERE'S TOO MANY OF THEM. I CAN'T—

MAN, MY HEAD'S SPINNING!

HE IS NO SPY... HE MUST BE AN ASSASSIN!!

THAT BOY IS WIPING THE FLOOR WITH OUR MEN!!

KEEP YOUR EYES PEELED! HE MIGHT HAVE ACCOMPLICES READY TO—

DON'T LET HIM GET NEAR THE BARONS!

YES, PROTECT US!

EVERY-BODY, GET DOWN! PROTECT THE BAR-ONS!

FIIIRE!!!

HEY! DO IT NOW!!

WAIT... IT WAS A BLUFF! HE'S ESCAPING!!

I WANT THIS BOY GONE— NOW!!

NAH! WE DO THIS!

THAT WAS A GENTLEMAN'S INVITATION TO A DUEL! IS THIS HOW YOU **RUFFIANS** RESPOND IN THESE SITUATIONS?!

HE'S A SAVAGE!!

YOU'RE THE ONE WHO SLAPPED ME IN THE FACE WITH A GLOVE!!

SSSSTT

NOOO, DON'T BREAK IT!

BO...!!

SO I HOPPED ONTO THE BALLOON AND LANDED. BUT THEN IT STARTED RAINING, YOU KNOW? SO I SLIPPED AND **COINCIDENTALLY** FELL INTO THAT TUB OF LARD THERE.

I WAS **COINCIDENTALLY** JUST HANGING AROUND ON MY BROOM, YOU KNOW, WHEN YOUR AIRSHIP BUMPED INTO ME.

SO I LOST MY BROOM, BUT YOUR SHIP WAS **COINCIDENTALLY** JUST LEAVING.

THAT'S ALL.

HEEEY!

OUT OF MY WAY, I'LL GO TEACH THIS WHIPPERSNAPPER A LESSON.

HE IS TAKING US FOR FOOLS!

I DON'T BELIEVE A WORD OF WHAT YOU JUST SAID! YOU'RE DEFINITELY A SPY!

PERHAPS THEY'RE VERY WELL HIDDEN. BEST TO STAY DIPLOMATIC JUST IN CASE.

NO, VIGILANN DOESN'T SEE ANYONE ELSE AROUND HERE.

WE DID NOT EXPECT ANYONE TO VISIT US.

BYE!

NO THANKS.

WHAT WOULD YOU SAY ABOUT JOINING US?

BUT WE WARMLY WELCOME YOU!

SO IF A GUY REFUSES TO HANG AROUND WITH YOU, YOU JUST GO AHEAD AND SKEWER HIM?!

HOLD ON A SECOND!

DON'T GET YOUR PANTIES IN A BUNCH!!

IS THAT SO? THEN WHAT ARE YOU DOING HERE?!

WAIT, WHAT? NO, YOU'VE GOT IT ALL WRONG. I'M NOT A WIZARD KNIGHT!

DON'T PLAY DUMB WITH US, WIZARD KNIGHT!

NOW, NOW. LET'S ALL JUST STAY CALM.
PAZZ, EITHER LET HIM GO, OR I WILL STAKE YOU ALONG WITH HIM!
NO! NO! NO!! I SAW IT FIRST, SO IT'S MINE!!
IF THE WIZARD KNIGHTS TRULY SENT ONE OF THEIR OWN TO COME GREET US, THEN SURELY HE ISN'T ALONE.
OFF YOU GO!!
HMPH!
WOOSH
KIIAAAH!
♪

CHAPTER 31 THE MERCHANT BARONS

THEIR EMINENCES SHOULD'VE BEEN PUT INTO A SMALLER AIRSHIP TO DISEMBARK BY NOW!

IF YOU DON'T WANT TO END UP MINCED LIKE THAT BIRD, I'D STRONGLY RECOMMEND YOU STOP DAWDLING AND GET BACK TO ATTENDING TO THE BARONS!

WE'RE HERE!

MY MELONS!!

MY BROOM!

SSS...

MAN, IT'S ALL SLIPPERY AND WET BECAUSE OF THE RAIN!! HOW AM I SUPPOSED TO—

!!

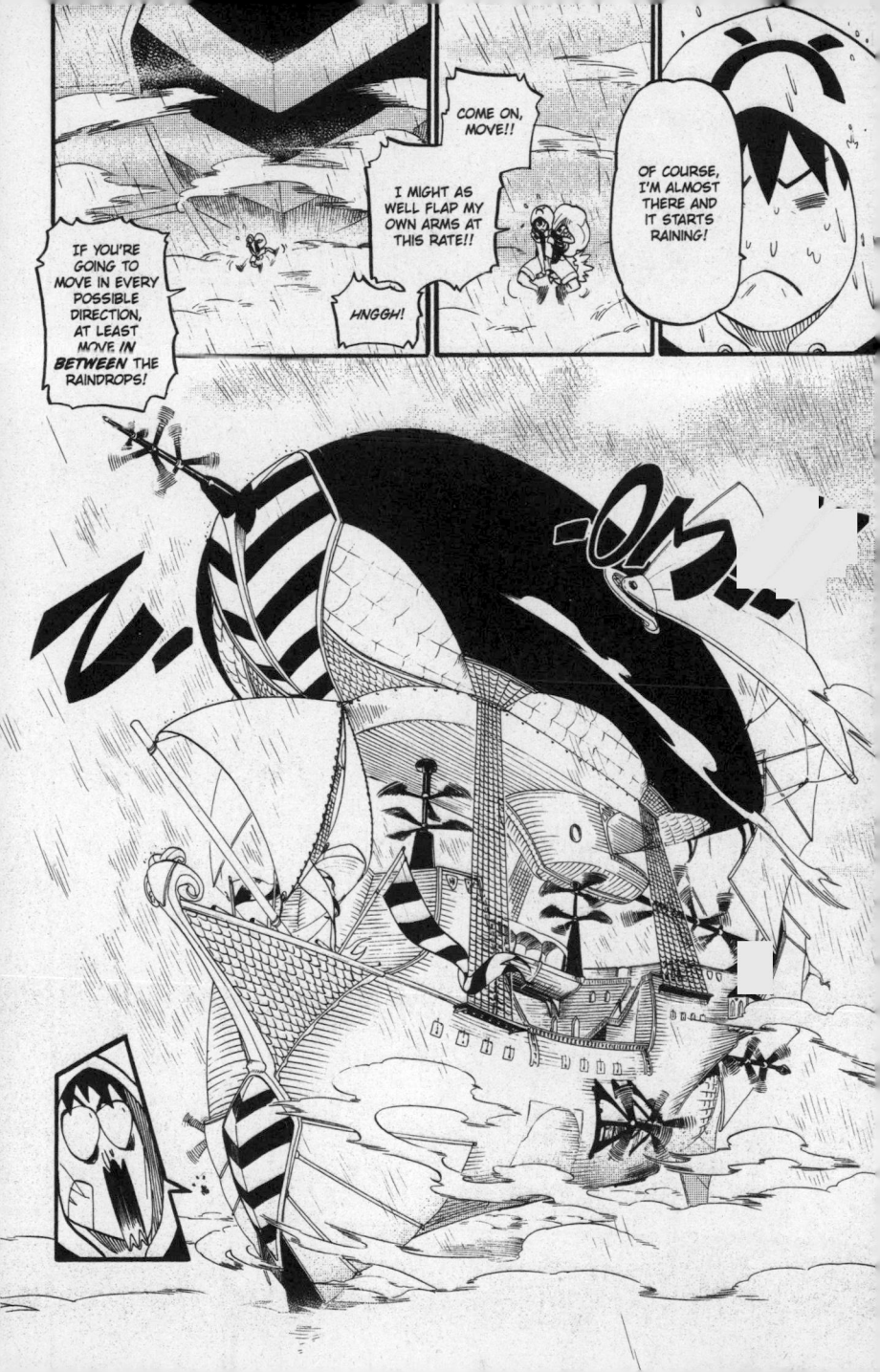

-Cyfandir-
Continent Islet

PLiC

I'LL DEFINITELY SEND YOU A MESSAGE THIS TIME.

AH, SUCH A TOUCHING GOODBYE AMONGST BRAVES! SO YOUNG! I UNDERSDAND WHY YOU KEEP WORRYING ABOUD 'IM EVERY DAY—

HURRY UP, HIDE YOUR HORNS, GO STRAIGHT AHEAD, DON'T GET LOST AND GOOD LUCK WITH YOUR RESEARCH.

PROMISE!

JIJI, DO SOMETHING! MY NOSE IS OBVIOUSLY BROKEN AND I MIGHT BLEED ON MISTRESS ALMA!

CR

OK

SURE, WHATEVER!

BUT ONCE YOU'RE PAST THAT, YOU NEED TO CONTINUE ON FOOT. GO IT?

OKAY, WE'VE BEEN FLYING FOR TWO DAYS, SO WE SHOULD BE AROUND HERE.

YOU NEED TO GO ALL THE WAY HERE AND THEN THROUGH THE WOODS, PAST SOME SMALL VILLAGES.

MY DEAR BRAVE SETH, JIJI AND YOURS TRULY PREPARED YOU A FEW DAYS' WORTH OF FOOD!

OH, THANKS!

TORQUE'S AFTER YOU NOW, SO YOU NEED TO KEEP A LOW PROFILE!

SURE, GOOD IDEA. AND AFTER THAT YOU CAN GO HANG OUT WITH SOME INQUISITORS AS WELL!

WHAT? CAN'T I JUST HITCH A RIDE WITH A CART GOING TO THE CASTLE?!

SOME CHEESE, SOME DRIED MEAT, FRESHLY BAKED BREAD FROM THIS MORNING ON YOUR DAILY DOSE OF FIVE FRUITS AND VEGETABLES—THREE PUMPKINS AND TWO WATERMELONS!

OH, YOU KNOW, JUST A FEW QUICK THINGS TO SNACK ON.

DUDE, THIS WEIGHS A TON! WHAT'D YOU EVEN PUT IN THIS?!

WHAT ?!

IT WAS ONLY A SECOND, BUT IT FELT LIKE **VISIONS** MORE THAN MEMORIES.

AND SOMETIMES, I—

BY THE WAY, I WAS ALSO ABLE TO SEE SOME IMAGES FLASH IN MY MIND AND HEAR SOME SOUNDS.

YEAH, WELL THAT'S JUST YOUR IMAGINATION WORKING OVERTIME!! IT'S NOT REAL, BUT IF YOU WANT TO DO SOMETHING WITH IT, JUST TAKE SOME NOTES, WRITE A BOOK AND BE DONE WITH IT!

WRITE A BOOK?!

LOOK, YOU'RE NOT GOING TO START BELIEVING IN PREMONITIONS NOW TOO, RIGHT?!

I NEVER SAID THEY WERE PREMONITIONS! I JUST SAID I SAW PLACES AND PEOPLE I DIDN'T KNOW.

SO YOU CAN SEE *THIS* COMING?!

GOOD, I'M STARVING!

COME ON! IF YOU STILL HAVE YOUR TEETH AFTER THAT KICK, THEN WE SHOULD GO EAT.

MISTRESS ALMA, DINNER IS READYYYY!!

...

YOU SEE THESE SCRATCHES HERE? A THAUMATURGE DID THIS TO ME.

BUT WHY? HE DIDN'T SEEM LIKE, YOU KNOW...

THAT'D COINCIDE WITH THE TIME I ALMOST LOST CONSCIOUSNESS. SO LIKE I TOLD YOU—PART OF ME IS LINKED TO THAT FREAKING WARD ON YOU!

THAT BLOW SHOULD HAVE KILLED ME! I ACTUALLY FELT LIKE I WAS DYING, ALMA. I COULD ACTUALLY FEEL IT!

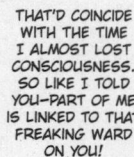

?!

ACTUALLY, PIODON WAS THE ONE WHO SAVED ME.

AT LEAST UNTIL YOUR WARD STOPPED IT.

AFTER THAT, IT ALL JUST STOPPED.

I DON'T KNOW HOW TO EXPLAIN IT, BUT IT WAS LIKE HE OPENED UP SOMETHING INSIDE OF ME *JUST ENOUGH* FOR ME TO SURVIVE THAT ATTACK.

AND FOR SOME REASON, I ALSO FELT IT FROM MILES AWAY! IT WAS HOSTILE!!

NOW THAT YOU MENTION IT, IT DID FEEL LIKE YOU WERE THERE WITH ME.

AND THEN THERE WAS ALSO THIS BOND I FELT WHEN WE WERE PROJECTED INTO, *UH*... I DON'T KNOW WHAT TO CALL IT. MY SPIRIT? MY MEMORIES?

NO, BUT CONSIDERING HOW MUCH HE LOOKED LIKE ME IT WOULD HAVE BEEN TOO MUCH OF A COINCIDENCE.

LOOK, SETH. BASED ON WHAT YOU DESCRIBED TO ME, THAT SOUNDED LIKE NOTHING MORE THAN AN ATTACK!

AND IT'S NOT LIKE INFECTED PEOPLE WITH HORNS ARE THAT RARE EITHER.

I DON'T KNOW IF I TRUST THIS GUY. LIKE HIS STORY AND HOW HE JUST APPEARED IN FRONT OF YOU. IT'S STRANGE.

WHAT IF IT WAS ACTUALLY HIM I WAS TRYING TO PROTECT YOU FROM?

BUT WHAT IF IT WASN'T A NEMESIS WHO INFECTED YOU?

LOOKS LIKE FOR SOME REASON PART OF ME IS LINKED TO THAT THING ON YOUR CHEEK. BUT YOU KNOW I DON'T REMEMBER MUCH FROM THAT TIME, SO I HAVE NO IDEA WHY THAT IS.

TCH... YOU'D THINK SO, BUT THEY'RE ONLY LOYAL— THAT'S IT!

THEY'D FOLLOW ME AROUND LIKE TWO PUPPIES EVEN IF I STARTED TRAFFICKING HUMAN ORGANS!

WOW... YOU REALLY TURNED THESE TWO AROUND!

MY THOUGHTS EXACTLY.

AND BELIEVE IT OR NOT, THEY'RE ACTUALLY DOING THEIR BEST TO HELP ME OUT.

MAYBE... BUT MEANWHILE THEY'RE A LOT MORE USEFUL HERE WITH YOU THAN STUCK IN SOME INQUISITION CELL.

IN RUMBLE TOWN, I MET THIS GUY, AND I THINK...

...HE'S MY BIG BROTHER.

ANYWAY, I DON'T THINK YOU NEED TO WORRY ABOUT THEM. THEY'RE A COUPLE OF BUFFOONS, BUT THEY DECIDED WE WERE FAMILY, SO...

THAT REMINDS ME, ALMA.

THEY TAKE CARE OF MY EVERY NEED AND DO WORK FOR TEN...

THOSE OTHER TWO BAD WEASELS TRIED TO TAKE ADVANTAGE OF MISTRESS ALMA'S WEAKENED STATE AFTER HER BRAVE BATTLE.

CAN YOU TRANSLATE? BECAUSE I AM *NOT* CATCHING A SINGLE WORD OF ALL THIS!!

ALSO, WEREN'T THERE FOUR OF THEM BEFORE?

WHAT?!

AND EBEN ABFTER EBRYDING BWE DID GEE ACCEPDED!!!

AND DOW, BY BRAVE BIBI AND BE ARE DA MOST...

SO I BEGGED DER DO LED VE BE HER AZZIZDAND!!

HUH...?

!!

STOP TALKING AND GO TAKE CARE OF THAT HOLE IN THE CEILING **YOU** MADE!!

PON!

SO I TOOK CARE OF THEM.

YEAH, YEAH, YOU DO THAT.

JIJI! TAKE THE HELM. WE'RE LEAVING.

YES MA'AM! WE'LL GO GET THE TOOLS THIS INSTANT!!

...THEY'RE THE TWO ASSISTANTS I TOLD YOU ABOUT.
I KNEW YOU WERE SLOW, KID, BUT...
'SCUSE ME?
I JUST WANTED AN EXPLANATION...
...NOT TO SEE HIS BUTT!!
NOW WE LOOK LIKE IDIOTS BECAUSE OF YOU!!
JIJI! WHAT THE HECK ARE YOU DOING?! I SAID 12! NOT 21!
LEAVE THEM TO ROT IN THAT CAGE? KILL 'EM MYSELF?
SO WHAT WOULD YOU SUGGEST I DO, HUH?
YOU FEEL LIKE YOU HAVE THE RIGHT TO DECIDE THE FATE OF ALL CRIMINALS NOW, BIG SHOT?
THE INQUISITOR NEVER CAME.
BUT THEY WERE TRYING TO ROB THE ISLET! YOU WERE ABOUT TO BRING THEM TO THE-
SURE, BUT THEY PUT THE ENTIRE VILLAGE IN DANGER AND-

JIJI! INTRO FORMATION NO. 12!

...

JULIVERT JENOH A.K.A. "JIJI"

DON BOSSMAN A.K.A. "BOSS"

CHAPTER 30
THE BRAVERY DUET

SHH HH...

W... SHH

JIJIII!!!

WHAT'D I DO?!

SEEETH !!!

I DON'T KNOOOW!!!

THAT'S MY STAFF YOU'RE ATTACKING, YOU IDIOT!!

AND I WAS ABOUT TO CUT THE CAKE I MADE FOR THE OCCASION.

YEAH, YEAH, YOU'RE A GOOD BOY!

I SWEAR ON MY BRAVETY THAT WE MEANT NO HARM...

SNIFF... MISTRESS ALMA, I ASKED MY BRAVE LITTLE JIJI TO HELP DECORATE THE INTERIOR OF YOUR HOME IN HONOR OF OUR BRAVE LITTLE SETH'S RETURN!

WILL SOMEONE PLEASE TELL ME WHAT IS GOING ON HERE?!

W...

WHAT EXACTLY DO THEY DO ANYWAY?

SOME OLD GUYS, SOME EVEN OLDER GUYS AND THEN SOME SUPER-OLD GUYS!

SO WHO ARE THESE COVEN WIZARDS?

BESIDES BEING OLD, I MEAN.

BEATS ME.

OTHER THAN STICKING THEIR NOSES WHERE THEY'RE NOT WANTED.

IF YOU ASK ME, THEY'RE ALL JUST A PRETENTIOUS BUNCH WHO'VE GOT NOTHING BETTER TO DO THAN TO START A SECRET CLUB TO WHILE AWAY THE LAST OF THEIR DAYS.

ALMAAA!!!

!!

WE'RE UNDER ATTACK!!

WELL, I WENT TO LOOK FOR GRIMM BUT COULDN'T FIND HIM.

HOW AM I EVEN SUPPOSED TO FLY SOMETHING LIKE THIS?!

YEAH, WELL **YOU** TRY FLYING ON THIS CRAPPY BROOM!!

READY?

TOOK YA LONG ENOUGH!

RIGHT. WHY NOT GET A MANICURE AND TAKE A DUMP WHILE YOU'RE AT IT TOO?

HRNGH!

GRAAH!

DIDN'T I TELL YOU WE HAD TO HURRY?! STOP WASTING TIME!!

STILL DOESN'T EXPLAIN WHY IT TOOK YOU THAT LONG.

MAYBE YOU'RE JUST AN AWFUL FLYER.

I, UH...

I KNOW...

BUT I ALSO COULDN'T FIND YAGA TO SAY GOODBYE.

THE WIZARD OF THE WEST HAS TAKEN OVER FOR ME WHILE I'M GONE, BUT IF ANY NEMESES FALL IN BOTH HER **AND** MY SECTOR, THINGS WILL GET DICEY VERY QUICKLY!

I'VE BEEN AWAY FROM POMPO HILLS FOR TOO LONG.

OH?

HE WOULDN'T TELL ME WHY, BUT GIVEN THE SITUATION SINCE RUMBLE TOWN, I WOULDN'T BE SURPRISED IF THE COVEN OF 13 IS HAVING AN URGENT MEETING.

YAGA? OH, HE WAS LEAVING THE ARTEMIS JUST WHEN I ARRIVED.

YOUR FIRST MISSION AS A MIRACLE WORKER...

YOU AND LIESELOTTE WILL BE LEAVING AT DAWN.

WE WILL PERFORM THE REVELATION CEREMONY FOR YOUR OWN MIRACLE LATER.

THAT IS FOR ANOTHER TIME. YOU CAME A LONG WAY TO GET HERE. REST FOR NOW...

BUT HOW?

YES, GENERAL.

ONLY YOU HAVE ENCOUNTERED THEM, AND SO LONG AS YOUR MEMORY HASN'T FADED, ONLY YOU CAN RECOGNIZE THEM.

...WILL BE TO FIND THE HORNED WIZARD AND HIS LITTLE GROUP.

I WOULDN'T WORRY ABOUT THAT, GENERAL. THEY'RE STILL VERY FRESH IN MY MIND.

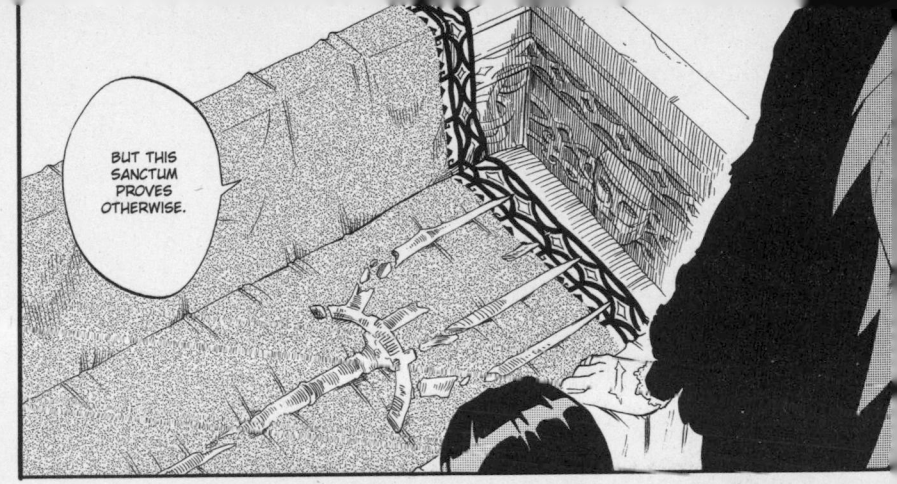

BUT THIS SANCTUM PROVES OTHERWISE.

SO, HOW COULD HE HAVE GONE UP AGAINST THE SUPERNATURAL FORCES WITH JUST ONE PITCHFORK?

THIS IS NOT A MAGICAL OBJECT NOR EVEN A COMPLEX WEAPON. IT IS MERELY A FARMER'S TOOL.

ONE OF HIS RELICS, YES.

THE PATREM INQUISITOR'S PITCHFORK?!

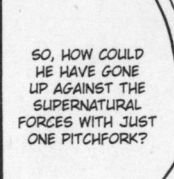

HIS SHEER WILL ALONE GRANTED HIM THE ABILITY TO PERFORM MIRACLES.

EXACTLY.

YOU'D NEED A MIRACLE TO PULL THAT OFF.

WE HOLD THE KEY TO **THE MIRACLE.**

WE THAUMATURGES ARE THE SPIRITUAL DESCENDANTS OF THIS **MIRACULOUS IRON WILL.** WE EACH REINCARNATE ONE OF HIS COUNTLESS ABILITIES.

COUPLED WITH THE STRENGTH OF THE THAUMATURGES, YOUR JUDGMENT WOULD GREATLY HELP US.

AS A PREVIOUS SUBORDINATE OF YOURS, I KNOW FULL WELL YOUR SKILLS AS AN *OBSERVER*, AND YOUR DEDICATION.

I WAS THE ONE WHO SUGGESTED THAT WE ADD YOU TO OUR RANKS.

THAT IS BECAUSE YOU KNOW YOUR LIMITS, CAPTAIN!

CONTRARY TO VON TEPPES, WHO RAN INTO BATTLE WITHOUT A PLAN OR EVEN THINKING FIRST OR USING HIS MIRACLE. WHAT A SHAME...

HERE I THOUGHT I WAS GOING TO BE EXECUTED.

I NEVER SAW *THIS* COMING!

A THAUMATURGE...

FOLLOW ME.

HOW A SIMPLE FARMER'S SON STOOD UP AGAINST THESE POWERFUL BEINGS! MANY CONSIDER THIS TO BE A MYTH—THAT A SINGLE INDIVIDUAL ARMED ONLY WITH HIS OWN WILL COULD WIN AGAINST MAGIC.

NEVER UNDERESTIMATE THE MAGIC OF WIZARDS WHO WILL BATTLE THAUMATURGES, FOR THEY ARE POWERFUL. REMEMBER THE TIMES WHEN THE WORLD WAS OVERRUN BY MAGIC, WIZARDS AND ENCHANTED OBJECTS!

...AND MEANWHILE THE MERCHANT BARONS ARE EXTENDING THEIR INFLUENCE BEYOND THE WESTERN STATES.

THE WIZARD KNIGHTS ARE PARADING THEIR STRENGTH...

WE ARE FACING TROUBLESOME TIMES THE LIKES OF WHICH NEITHER OF US HAVE EVER EXPERIENCED BEFORE. HISTORY IS ONCE AGAIN IN MOTION— THE DOMITORS HAVE COME OUT OF HIDING.

AT THE SAME TIME, WE IN THE INQUISITION ARE BUSY TAKING CARE OF OUR OWN CITIZENS' FATE.

AS SUCH, TODAY ENDS THE PEACEFUL EXISTENCE OF CAPTAIN DRAGUNOV, THE WATCHER OF POMPO HILLS...

MY THAUMATURGES ARE HARD AT WORK IN ALL FOUR CORNERS OF PHARENOS REAFFIRMING OUR POSITION AND REASSURING THE PEOPLE THAT WE CAN GUARANTEE THEIR SAFETY.

DECISIONS I AM BURDENED TO MAKE.

BUT IN ORDER TO MAINTAIN THIS FRAGILE EQUILIBRIUM, HARD DECISIONS ARE SOMETIMES NECESSARY.

BUT THE POPULACE IS POINTING FINGERS AT THE INQUISITION IN ITS ENTIRETY, USING A DETAILED REPORT EXPLAINING THE EVENTS THAT HAPPENED IN RUMBLE TOWN.

CAPTAIN OF MARBOURG'S ACTIONS HAVE LEFT A FELL BLEMISH UPON OUR REPUTATION.

AS YOU WELL KNOW, THE INQUISITION IS CURRENTLY FACING A VERY REAL CRISIS OF FAITH.

IT WAS *YOUR* REPORT, AFTER ALL.

I WON'T BORE YOU WITH THE DETAILS, MY DEAR CAPTAIN, AS YOU KNOW THEM BETTER THAN ANYONE...

IT'S A VERY PERCEPTIVE REPORT CONTAINING NUMEROUS ACCOUNTS AND PROOF OF THE COMPLICITY OF THE INQUISITION'S RESOURCES IN THE DOMITOR WIZARD'S ATTACK AS WELL AS THE FALL OF THE NORTH-EASTERN SUBURB.

NOW, STAND.

IF IT HAD BEEN MY WISH TO HEAR YOUR EXCUSES OR EVEN JUST BLAME YOU, I WOULD HAVE DONE SO IN AN OFFICIAL MANNER AT OUR HEADQUARTERS— NOT IN THE MIDDLE OF A GLACIER.

THOUGH SOMEONE OF YOUR INTELLECT COULD HAVE GUESSED, I'M SURE.

IT WAS NEVER MY INTENTION TO—

I DON'T NEED YOU TO EXPLAIN YOURSELF, DRAGUNOV!

GENERAL, I SIMPLY WISHED TO SHINE LIGHT ON ALL THE VIOLATIONS COMMITTED BY CAPTAIN KONRAD OF MARBOURG AND PREVENT THIS FROM EVER REPEATING ITSELF IN THE FUTURE!

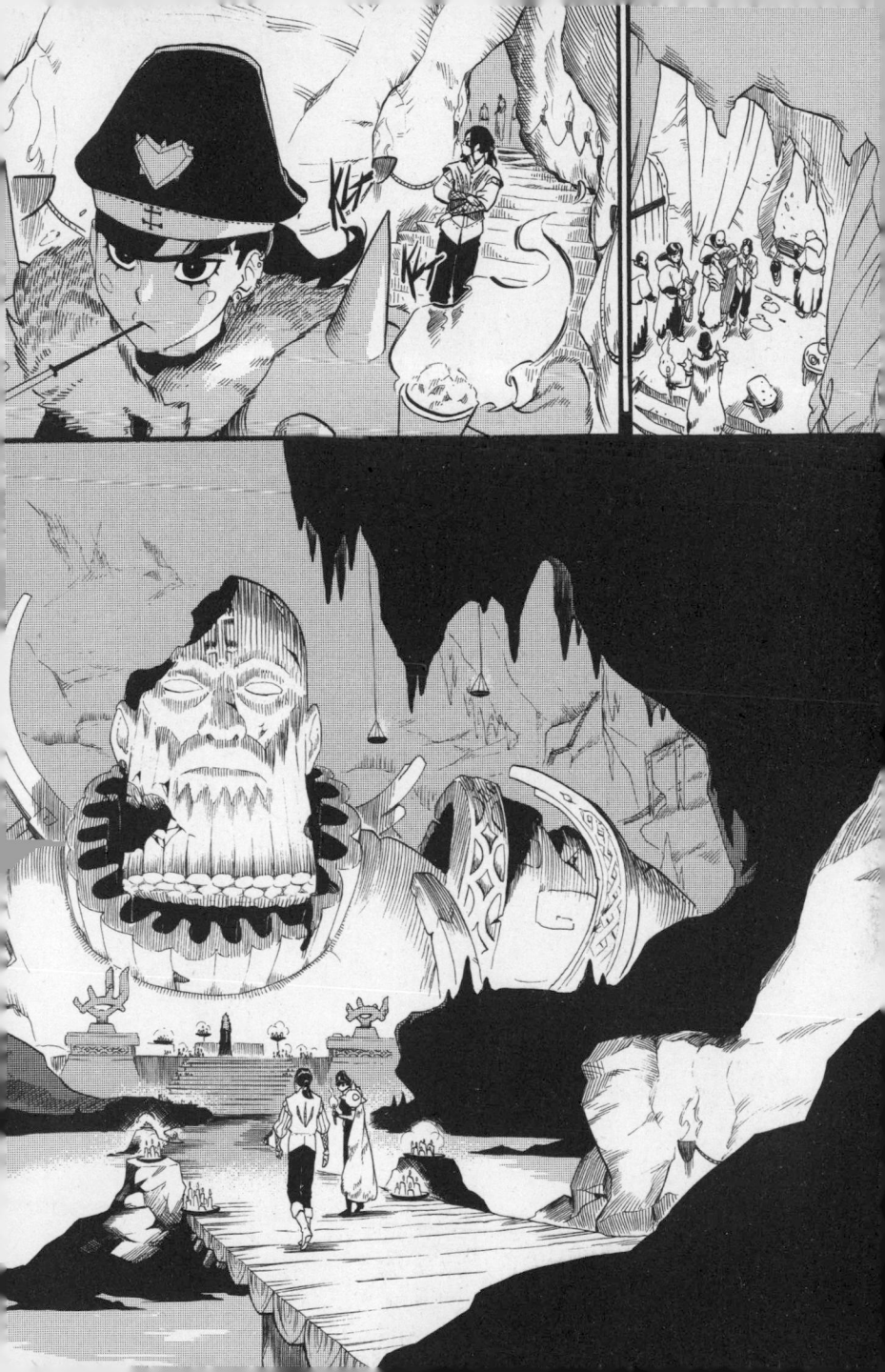

YEAH, YEAH...

NO REFUNDS AND NO EXCHANGES ON DISCOUNTED ITEMS!

AND I'LL TAKE THE BLACK GLOVES AND THE BROOM ON THE BOTTOM SHELF.

IN THAT CASE, GIVE ME THAT LITTLE CAULDRON THERE.

!!

WITH THE MERCHANDISE YOU ALREADY HAVE, THAT BRINGS YOU TO A TOTAL OF 132 DIMES!

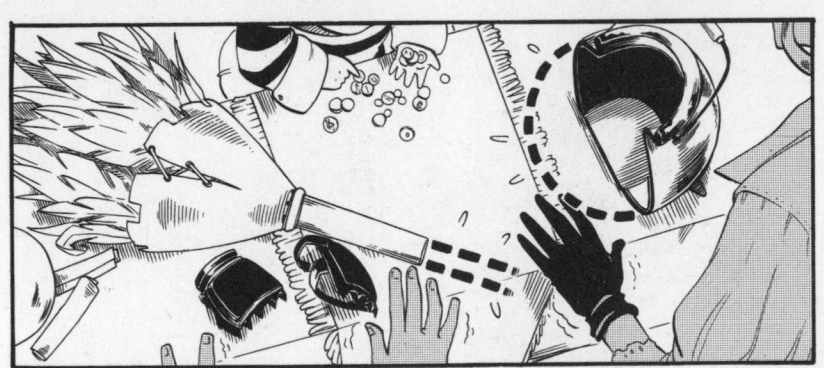

OW! OW! HONEY! MY BOY! I'M BEING HARASSED!!

FOR REAL THIS TIME!

AHA! I KNEW YOU WIZARDS WERE DIRTY PEOPLE!

I'M NOT GOING TO CLEAN ANY ROOMS!!

WHAT AM I SUPPOSED TO DO WITH HALF A BROOM?!

CLEAN HALF A ROOM?

WHERE'S THE REST?!

YEAH, DUH! I TOLD YOU THEY WERE HALF OFF, RIGHT?

SO, WHAT BRINGS YOU TO MY HUMBLE ABODE? MS. WITCH ALMA, NOBLE GUARDIAN OF THE SOUTH OF POMPO HILLS AND HER TRUSTY—

KEEP TALKING, BROWNNOSER! SEE WHAT HAPPENS!

OH, RIGHT! SILLY ME AND MY SELECTIVE MEMORY! I GOT THAT FROM MY WIFE! REALLY, SHE'S GOING TO BE THE DEATH OF ME SOMEDAY!

HE CHANGED HIS MIND REALLY FAST!

DID YOU FORGET EVERYTHING WE DID FOR YOU AT POMPO HILLS?!

?

OH, WELL THAT WOULD EXPLAIN ALL THESE STRANGE-LOOKING HOUSEHOLD PRODUCTS!

MAGIC?

NO, WE MEANT WHY ARE YOU RUNNING A MAGIC STORE CONSIDERING YOU'RE, YOU KNOW...*YOU*! SURE, THE ARTEMIS IS OPEN TO ANYONE, BUT STILL...

SO WHAT ARE YOU DOING HERE?

WELL, AFTER OUR LITTLE SHOP IN RUMBLE TOWN WENT DOWN, WE FOLLOWED A GROUP OF—

WELL! EVERYTHING HERE ON THE SHELVES BEHIND ME IS HALF OFF!

LOOK, WE DIDN'T COME HERE TO CHITCHAT. WE NEED SOME STUFF, SO TELL US WHAT'S CHEAP!

OR FREE! I'M OKAY WITH FREE...!

SORRY FOR THE LONG WAIT! WE'RE STILL GETTING USED TO OUR NEW STORAGE ROOM!

BUT I'M HERE NOW! SO WHAT CAN I DO FOR...

WE ONLY BOUGHT THIS PLACE THREE DAYS AGO, YOU SEE.

NO, I MEANT DID **THEY** AGREE TO THIS DEAL?!

IT'S NOT LIKE I HAD A CHOICE! AFTER YOU LEFT, I—

ABOUT THAT! YOU REALLY TOOK ON TWO ASSISTANTS? VOLUNTARILY?

WHAT'CHA TRYIN' TO SAY?! YOU IDIOT!

...YOU?

I HAVEN'T TOUCHED YOU!!

NOT YET!

HEEEELP! I'M BEING HARASSED! HONEY! MY SON! RUN FOR YOUR LIVES!!

BUT COME SAVE ME FIRST...

SAVE MEEE !!!

TWI'T

TWI'T

...A PENDULUM WITH A PARCHMENT-RETRACTABLE CHAIN...

SO WHAT ARE WE LOOKING FOR?

...AND A BELT TO STORE EVERYTHING.

LET'S SEE...

WHEN DID YOU LEARN HOW TO USE ALL OF THOSE?

A DOUBLE SEATER BROOM, CONTAINMENT PARCHMENTS...

DOC LEFT HIS AIRSHIP BEHIND AND THERE'S NO WAY I CAN PAY HIM BACK FOR A NEW ONE, SO I'M GOING TO GET HIM, UH...I DON'T KNOW? MAYBE A TRIPLE NECKTIE? OR A TRASH CAN. THE MAN LOVES A GOOD TRASH CAN.

THEY'RE FOR MÉLIE. SHE LOST A LOT OF EQUIPMENT IN RUMBLE TOWN AND IT KIND OF FEELS LIKE IT'S MY FAULT, SO...

WHAT ABOUT DOC?

UGH... I SEE WHERE THIS IS GOING!

ME? I BARELY GOT ANY MONEY FROM THOSE NEMESES AND AFTER BUYING ALL THIS FOR MÉLIE AND DOC, I'LL PROBABLY HAVE NOTHING LEFT.

WHAT ABOUT YOU? YOU'RE NOT GOING TO RUN OFF TO THE WIZARD KNIGHTS UNPREPARED, ARE YOU?

HERE, THIS BROOM SHOULD DO.

AND I'VE ALREADY GOT THE OTHER TWO MORONS TO PAY FOR NOW! AAARGH!!

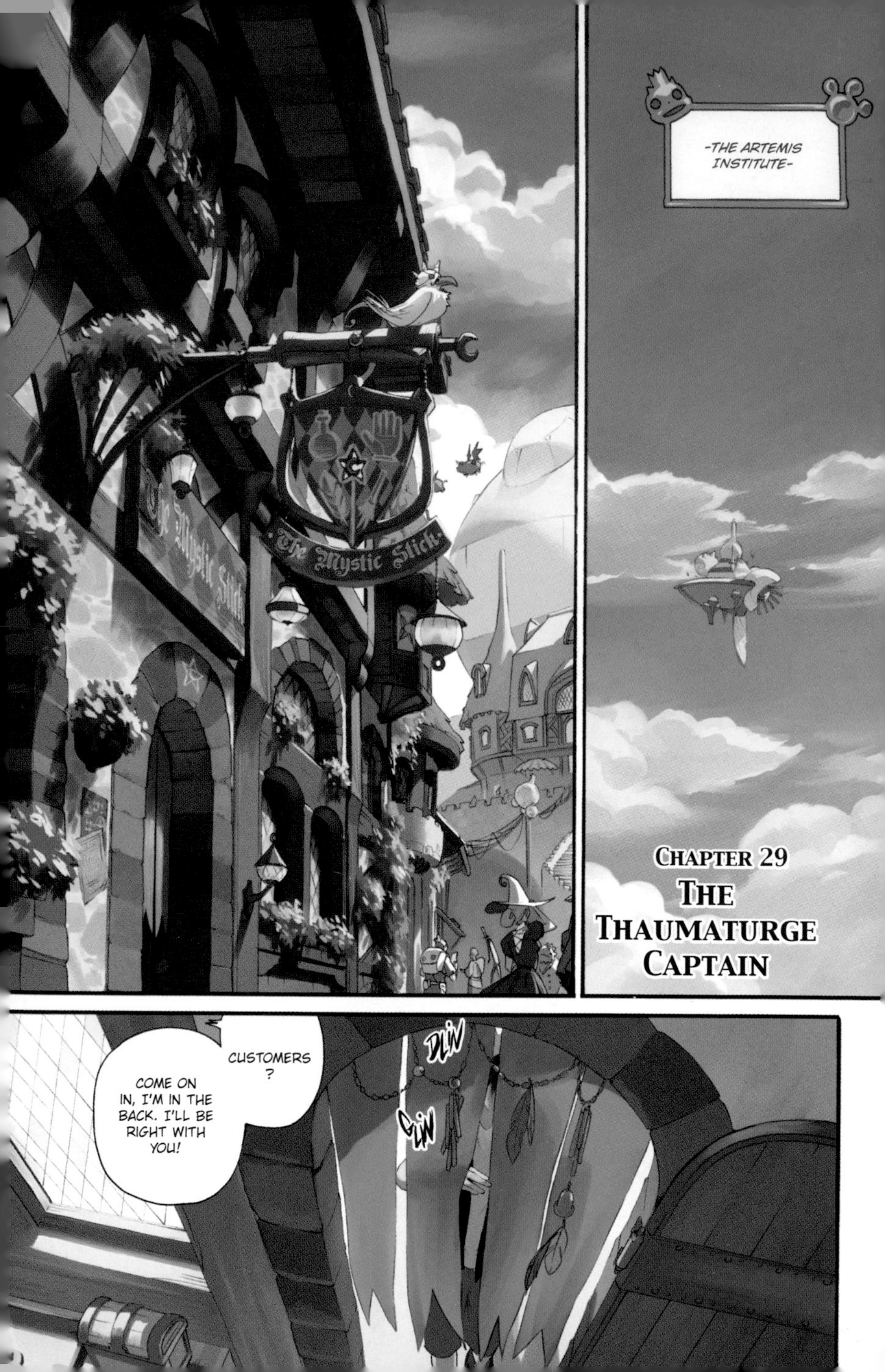

-THE ARTEMIS INSTITUTE-

CHAPTER 29
THE THAUMATURGE CAPTAIN

CONTENTS

N

Elefranche

Solok

Hvittland

Atlanty

-HIGHER VIBRION-

Seap

Ynys Tertynot

Feidh A

-INLANDSIS-

Pelery

Shidoli

Branoc

Caislean Ceoch

Caerlion

Caislean M

Cerboi

Cloch

Lysburry

-LOWER VIBRION-

Ynys Niwlog

Sylveribe

-CYFANDIR-

Triskelion Ba

Castell Tris

Allialy

Pharénos nord oriental

Meden-Vale

Arfodyl

Nordour

le Denteli Errant

Anse des Derniers

Ondes

Spyll

Renoran

Ujji

Valice

Cap-Val

Solsi

Bourgponant

-WESTERN STATES-

-THE CROSSING

Castellar

Malsudant

Papo-Liori

Boscane

Valevino

Vissilly

Défilé des Lames

Lagoss

Agoree

Arène

-Solsi-
CITY-STATE OF THE
MERCHANT BARONS.
MAIN PORT OF THE
WESTERN STATES.

-Caislean Merlin-
CITADEL OF THE WIZARD
KNIGHTS.
CAPITAL OF THE LANDS OF
CYFANDIR.

The Pharenos
North Occidental

Les Ulfhednars

Arcadien

-GRAND TUULINEN-

Nanuk

Brikh

Blanche

Golfe de Strom

Septentrium

Runik

La pince

Cratt

Starigrav

Cape-Koillinen

Bôme

Dois

Vivacyne

Florvance

Cermont

Pharénos nord oriental

Relixe

Mer Grise

Convictis

-HORIZON-

ig

Port-aux-Brumes

Lisse

Hortum

Golfe du Béat

Llux

Canardy

Delft

-ESTRIE KINGDOMS-

Evicure

stone

Baie Grise

Béarn

Orcheland

Brehel

Maune

Port-Sud

Anse de l'Hysope

Trinan

Chandellion

Valay

Sauge

Dombour

Dumbour

Aigreroy

Hargeuil

Ouissant

-HORIZON
INTERIOR-

Fort-Cedrat

Les Traines

Sariett

L'Artémis

Boscade

Prosperity
"Rumble Town"

Saich

Cerfeuil

Pompo Hills

Islet 1

Islet 21

Archipel Coulant

-Bôme-
INQUISITION HQ
FORTRESS CAPITAL OF THE
ESTRIE KINGDOMS.

Pharénos "Grand Sud"

Desert Port

RADIANT

TONY VALENTE